BITTER HARVEST

by

Frederic
and
Sandra Halbert

D1572016

WILLIAM B. EERDMANS PUBLISHING COMPANY
GRAND RAPIDS, MICHIGAN

Library of Congress Cataloging in Publication Data

Halbert, Frederic, 1945-
  Bitter Harvest.

  1. Cattle — Feeding and feeds. 2. Feed contamination —
Michigan. 3. Polybrominated biphenyls — Toxicology —
Michigan. 4. Halbert, Frederic, 1945- 5. Halbert,
Sandra, 1943- 6. Farmers — Michigan — Battle Creek
region — Bibliography. I. Halbert, Sandra, 1943-
joint author. II. Title.
SF203.H25   636.2'08'9431   78-23531
ISBN 0-8028-7039-2

BITTER HARVEST

1

THE POSSUM-BELLIED cattle-hauler pulled off the highway at the blue and white sign that read "Halbert Dairy Farm," and hissed to a stop in the driveway.

A stocky trucker climbed down from the cab and exchanged a casual greeting with Ted Halbert, who had emerged from the shadows of the barn. "Where can I pull up to load the cows?" he asked, mopping his forehead in the heat.

"The loading ramp is over there," Ted replied, motioning to the front of the barn. "We'll let the cows out into the holding area, and then herd them onto the trucks at the ramp. My son will be over there to give you a hand."

Nodding, the driver returned to his truck and backed it in place against the ramp. "Let 'em come!" he hollered.

A trickle of pathetically thin animals started hesitantly down the alleyway. They bore no resemblance to the vigorous stampedes of movies and television commercials. Confused by the strange surroundings, they stopped short of the trailer and stood eyeing it suspiciously. Impatiently, the driver returned to the cab for his electric cattle prod. Clambering up the side of the loading ramp he made his way through the unsuspecting knot of cattle and into the alley behind the last of them. He poked the stragglers, and with a bellow of alarm at the jolt they lurched forward into the group, scattering in the general direction of the truck. Using the prod again and again helped matters along further.

At that moment Rick Halbert appeared. "Hey! You don't have to use that prod on them," he yelled. Quickly he walked over to the defensive and frightened cows. "Come on, girls," he said softly, "Come on." Slowly, the terrified cattle began to walk toward him. It was the last time they would go through this ritual with him.

Less than a year ago it had been for milking and feeding that Rick spoke to the cows. Now he was helping them board a truck to leave the farm forever. The cows had been our meal ticket, of course. In the past they had always provided an income for our family, for Rick's parents, his brother Mark, and for five hired men who worked on the farm. But I could also remember Rick's love for these animals and his pride in their healthy appearance. Lining up at a feeder they had been uniformly glossy-coated and bright-eyed.

6   All that was before the PBB contamination. Polybrominated biphenyl—PBB: the initials that were fast becoming a household word in Michigan—inadvertently mixed with a feed supplement had caused the mysterious ailment that had brought us to this terrible afternoon, watching these once-beautiful animals plod slowly toward their death, ears drooping, coats dull and coarse, patches of hair missing from some faces and necks to reveal a peculiar elephant-like skin, many stumbling over distorted hoofs.

The process of discovering what the problem was and how it had happened had been an exhausting and frustrating one. Perhaps the answer would never have been found had it not been for Rick's persistent curiosity, the inquiring scientific urge that had led him to begin a career in chemical engineering before other sides of his personality had asserted themselves and brought him back to the farm. But whatever exhilaration Rick had felt at solving the puzzle was no longer evident as we watched this sickly procession.

"My God! what happened to these animals?" the driver asked, noticing for the first time their condition. Instinctively he recoiled from contact with them. "Is it contagious?"

"You can't catch anything by handling them for this short a time," Rick reassured him. "These cows ate half a pound of fire retardant in contaminated feed. It's a miracle they're alive at all." Reaching out to the small cow nearest him, jostling weakly against the others, he whispered, "It's almost done, Pee Wee, it's almost over."

Almost over. For Pee Wee and the rest of the ailing herd, which had numbered four hundred only eleven months ago, that was the grim truth. For us and for many other Michigan farmers and residents, the story that had begun to unfold with a vague uneasiness about dropping milk production on a September afternoon in 1973 would not end for a while. Even if the worst fears of some who had studied the PBB contamination and its consequences were unfounded, the way it had happened and the obstacles to discovering it gave one scant confidence that such a disaster would never be repeated.

2

THE METALLIC THUD of the pickup door closing was my
signal to get lunch on the table. In the two years that we had
been working on the family farm, I had learned to cope with the
busy but irregular schedule a dairy farmer keeps. Early each
morning Rick would leave the house, drive five miles to the
main farm and milking setup, and plan the day's work assignments with his father and brother. Since much of his daily work
consisted of machinery repair and animal health care, Rick
often came home for a meal because there was a lull in his
activities, not necessarily because it was the appointed time to
eat. Before coming into the kitchen, Rick would change his
clothes; it was a practice we had agreed upon to keep as much
of the barnyard smell as we could out of the main part of the
house. I listened to the regular rhythms of his homecoming as
the children scurried through the kitchen with their tableware.

"We'll be ready in about five minutes," I began, but my
cheerful greeting turned to caution when I caught a glimpse of
Rick's face. "Why don't you read the paper while you're waiting?"

"The cows still won't eat a thing. They just stand in their
stalls at the milking stations, and they won't even look at the
parlor feed." Parlor feed is a high-protein supplement offered
to the cows in the milking parlor while the machines coax the
milk from their udders. His face a map of the morning's frus-

trations, Rick put down the newspaper unread. When I called him for lunch, he was reading a veterinary textbook from the living room bookshelf.

"We've lost hundreds of pounds of milk in a few days, and I can't figure out why the cows won't eat. I thought it might be the heat, but it's cooled off now. I just don't understand."

Lunch over, Rich headed back to the barn, too preoccupied even to say good-bye to Stephanie, waiting under the maple tree in the front yard for the kindergarten bus. I dismissed the problem from my mind; every good dairyman goes through unexplained dips in milk production now and again, and the whole situation would probably work itself out in a few days. The drive from our house to the original two hundred acres Ted Halbert had bought thirty years ago passed acreage which father and sons had added to the farm over the intervening years. The sprawling patchwork of fields was laced together by blacktop and rimmed by the homes of commuters and hobby farmers who had fled nearby Battle Creek and Kalamazoo for scenery and quiet.

Like the commuters Rick had left the city, too, but unlike them he had also given up his job. Scarcely two years ago, he had resigned a successful position as an engineer at the Dow Chemical complex in Midland. We had sold our subdivision home there and bought an old farmstead five miles north of his parents' farm, near Delton, Michigan, ten miles from Battle Creek. His parents had been disappointed at what seemed to them an abandonment of his natural aptitude for science; but he fit easily into the routine of managing the farm with his father, a life he had known from childhood, and only the monthly flood of engineering and amateur radio magazines might have tipped off a casual acquaintance to his educational background.

We had soon accustomed ourselves to the long hours required of the dairy farmer—virtually a twenty-four-hour day, if one considers that he must always be on call in case a cow has a calving problem, or the milking system breaks down, or if one of the regular milkers suddenly takes sick. Morning milking, which began at midnight, ran to about 6 a.m.; and included observation of the cows in each barn for illness and removal of animal wastes. Two men could handle the entire 400 cow herd at a milking, with another man coming to work at 6:00 to feed the cows as milking finished. After the morning chores, the two morning milkers left for the day, and at 7:00 the rest of the men came to work, getting their job assignments for the day in the barn office before work.

The daylight hours were spent ministering to the needs of the cattle, milking them again in the afternoon from 1–5, hauling manure out of the under-barn pits and spreading it on the fields, repairing machinery, fences, and barns, moving cattle or young stock from one barn to the next according to the system of barns arranged by the ages of the livestock. A bow-roofed red hay barn at Rick's father's place served as a calf nursery; a white toolshed across the lane from the haybarn housed four-month-old calves; and a faded pink barn at the farm a half mile away to the east, where Ted's father had once lived, housed six-month-old calves and older. A second farmstead to the north housed nine-month-old calves in an old, remodeled basement barn. Heifers ready to breed were returned to a metal freestall barn and lot behind the big red hay barn on Ted's place until they were ready to calve. "Springers," as the first calf heifers were called because of the loosening of the ligaments in their hindquarters preparatory to the birth of the calf, were taken to the dry-cow lot at the new milking setup two miles away to the north on the state highway. From this point onward, the animals would stay at the milking setup, moving from one lot to another within the six-lot system of barns according to the amount of milk they produced during the ten months each year they were in milk.

The rest of the buildings on the sprawling patchwork of the farm were used to store baled hay and equipment; the quaint, horse-tilled fields had been enlarged to accommodate modern farm equipment by the removal of the fencerows and lanes, and now supported the thousand head of cattle. It had often been impossible to purchase contiguous fields and adjoining farms, so the entire farm stretched from the junction of the highway and the county hardtop to Rick's place, some five miles northwestward. It was not uncommon to see the farm's heavy green farm machinery plodding from one field to the next in planting or harvest season.

Arriving at the barn Rick went straight to the milkhouse to read the dipstick on the two-thousand-gallon bulk milk tank before the milk hauler came. Apprehensively, he climbed the ladder, only to have his worst suspicions confirmed. Production had dropped another four hundred pounds in twenty-four hours. He climbed down and walked slowly to the barn office to check the feed records in the filing cabinet there. While he was shuffling through the papers, his father walked in. Without greeting him Rick said, "I checked the dipstick. We're down another four hundred pounds."

"I know—I checked it too." There was no alarm in the older man's voice; he had seen similar production drops several times in three decades of dairying. "Don't get excited; you know how daily production can vary. Things will probably turn around in a day or so."

"But it's been three days already," Rick replied. "And I don't see the cows eating anything. There just doesn't seem to be any improvement."

"Remember when we had to dispose of the herd because of Brucellosis? That was the worst thing that ever could have happened to us, and we recovered. Whatever the problem is now, you'll probably forget all about it as soon as the production comes back up."

"Well, I'll check to see which cows need breeding," Rick said. "Maybe something will show up in the next day or so. But if nothing improves we'd better call Dr. Jackson." Grabbing a dog-eared notebook from the desk top, he left for the milking parlor. Spotlessly cleaned by the morning milkers, the empty parlor was almost eerie with its pipes, hoses, and strange gadgets. Soon it would awaken to the pulsing sounds of the milking machines, the jangle of neckchains on the cattle, the jostling of the cows, and through it all the music from the portable radio on a shelf near the door. Rick would have been pleased to escort an Agriculture Department inspector through the facility at a moment's notice.

Springing up the steps at the end of the parlor, he walked carefully into the slippery 30 × 90 foot holding area for cattle, which connected the milking area to the barns. He wanted to check the cows for something besides breeding. Reaching the first barn, he turned to the heavy metal gate, pushed it aside, and went in. As if by design, a small open space rippled around him as he moved through the cattle. They retained enough of the ancient wild instinct that their initial reaction to man was one of shyness.

Soon black-and-white faces surrounded him, thrusting long, raspy, curious tongues into his pockets and slobbering on his back as though trying to consume his blue denim jacket. He reached out to the nearest cow, a glossy-coated three-year-old with a mass of curly hair on her poll. "Good bise," he said softly, scratching her behind the ears, where no cow or post could reach. The cow stretched her neck in appreciation. A shoving match erupted at the back of the circle of curious cows; two animals of similar herd rank were vying for a calf-sized space in the circle. Rick smiled at this display of bovine problem-solving, and waved his hands. Like huge dry leaves before a fall wind, the cows dispersed, scrambling frantically, backing into freestalls, aisles, and each other, their momentary bravery forgotten.

Rick resumed his walk through the barn, sometimes affectionately slapping a flank or pausing to examine a sore hock or a lame foot. At the far end of the barn, near the water tank, he found a familiar, low-slung cow with a sad face and drooping Brahman-like ears. She was not an ideal Holstein; her conformation was awry, and her ears had never looked like they should belong to a dairy cow. One of the hired men had begun to call her Flopsy as a calf, and the name had stuck.

In spite of her visible shortcomings, Flopsy was a good producer. She was also so friendly that she often followed Rick around the barn as he made his rounds. She was an unusually gentle cow, a calming influence in the milking parlor when there were new heifers to break into the daily routine. As he scratched her ears, she browsed down the front of his coveralls, snorting softly, like a big dog checking to see where he'd been all day. He ran his hand along the cow's side. She was in good shape. Her brisket carried only a small amount of fat, and her full body showed that she was within a month of delivering her third calf.

The impatient cow bunted him out of his reverie. "You teach that calf how to be a good milker, old girl," he said, scratching Flopsy's ears once more. Several inquisitive tongues were again searching his back pockets. He returned to his examination of the cows in the barn, attended now by Flopsy. When he had finished and slipped back through the gate, Flopsy stood silently nearby, as if awaiting his return.

The next barn was where the top-producing animals were kept. Except for a few curious cows which came up to him, the barn was very quiet—almost too quiet for midday. Rick began to walk the length of the barn, looking again for any unusual behavior. Suddenly he stopped. The cow in front of him looked as if she had been crying; there were streaks running from her eyes down her cheeks. He checked her for signs of infection, especially pinkeye. There was none of the clouding that usually accompanied pinkeye; and both of the cow's eyes had been running. It was unusual for a cow to have a foreign object in both eyes. Rick searched for another set of symptoms. Maybe she had infectious bovine rhinotracheitis—IBR, a flu-like disease which causes abortions in cattle. Standing near the cow's **13** shoulder, he felt her ears and made a mental note to bring the thermometer back and check her for fever, although she felt normal to the touch. All of their calves had been vaccinated against IBR, but maybe she had been purchased from someone else and somehow missed the inoculation.

Satisfied that this cow had no other symptoms, he walked farther along the feed alley. Again he was greeted by a long, tear-streaked face. He checked the second cow, and found a similar set of symptoms—both eyes watering, no pinkeye, no noticeable fever. As he continued his inspection, he concluded that nearly every one of the hundred cows in this barn had the same symptoms. What could this be? One possibility that came to mind was iodine poisoning. He had seen cattle treated with massive doses of iodine for a condition called lumpy jaw develop the tears that were characteristic of iodine toxicity. Puzzled by his discovery, he began to walk back to the holding area.

The cows hardly seemed to notice him as he walked slowly behind them; but he was watching them very closely. Something still did not seem right. About halfway back to the holding area it dawned on him. Not one of the resting cows was chewing her cud. He doubled back to make certain that he hadn't missed any of the cows, but the second trip through the barn was no more cheering than the first.

Cows chew their cud even in their sleep. As ruminates, they

have a fermentation stomach filled with microbes, which digest the cellulose found in plant leaves and stems. In order to prepare this roughage for the digestive system, they regurgitate the coarse material, and chew it over and over until it can pass on to the conventional stomach for further digestion. A barn full of cows none of which was chewing her cud was a serious cause for concern: it meant that the cows' digestive systems had come to a virtual halt.

Rick was troubled as he hurried over to the barn office to call the veterinarian. Within an hour, Dr. Jackson had pulled into the driveway and was unloading his instruments. He was a seasoned animal doctor, a bit stooped in the shoulders from years of difficult work, but wiry and energetic beyond his fifty-seven years.

"There's no reason for these cattle to have IBR," Dr. Jackson said after finishing his examination of the tearing cows. "I vaccinated them all myself, and the vaccine came from several suppliers, so we can't blame it on a bad batch of vaccine. I just don't think this is IBR, but I'll be hanged if I know *what* it is. These cattle don't act like any I've ever seen before. No cuds, no appetites, no fever—I don't know what they've got."

Jackson was too dedicated a veterinarian, too tenacious a diagnostician, to let the mysterious ailment go unexplained. He glanced at Rick as they walked back together to the milkhouse. "I think it might be a good idea to have the vets from the Michigan Department of Agriculture come around and take a look at your herd, Rick. There might be something in their experience that could help get this pinned down. What do you think?"

Rick nodded his approval. "You know, I'm still bothered that they aren't even touching that parlor feed. I wonder if that has something to do with it. I think I'll give Farm Bureau Services a call."

"Good idea," the doctor replied, packing up his instruments.

Michigan Farm Bureau Services is a cooperative organization established to meet the feed, fuel, and supply needs of the farm community statewide. We had been purchasing our feed from them for years. As soon as the doctor left, Rick dialed their telephone number in Lansing.

"Could I speak with your staff nutritionist, please?"

The receptionist routed Rick's call to a Dr. McKean.

"Dr. McKean, my name is Rick Halbert. My father and I have a dairy herd near Battle Creek, and we've been using Farm Bureau's #402 complete ration pelleted feed in the parlor."

"I'm familiar with that feed, yes."

"Well, since shortly after we took delivery of the last load of #402 five days ago, the cattle have been refusing to eat the pellets or their other feed. Their production has dropped drastically for the past several days—we've lost 400 more pounds of milk each day since then.

"Sounds like an inappetance problem. What other rations are you feeding them?"

"They get corn silage three times a day in feeders that run along one side of their freestall barns; and we've been top-dressing the silage with high-moisture corn."

"Where have you been getting the high-moisture corn?" Dr. McKean asked. "Much of last year's high-moisture corn was too wet. Your corn is probably moldy."

"We buy the corn from a neighbor," Rick replied. "We've been using it for months as a topdressing, but we haven't had any problem with anorexia till this past week."

"What kind of mineral do you use?"

"Farm Bureau's 12% phosphorus dairy mineral."

"Well," said Dr. McKean, "there can be a lot of problems associated with loss of appetite. Since we haven't had any other complaints about #402, I suspect one of your other rations is at fault. If it'll make you feel better, I'll send somebody over to take samples of the feed so we can analyze it. Can you get it ready by tomorrow morning?"

"Yes, we'll be waiting." Then Rick added, "I've been looking through some veterinary texts on my own, and I've made a list of contaminants which might have gotten into the feed by accident."

"You'd better leave diagnostic work to a trained veterinarian, Mr. Halbert."

Rick ignored the remark. "Some of the symptoms would suggest contamination of the feed by the accidental inclusion of machine lubricants, specifically chlorinated naphthalenes, during the pelleting process. I suppose you've heard of 'X Disease.'"

"Yes, though I've never seen a case of it," Dr. McKean answered.

"What do you use in the feed plant to lubricate the pelleting equipment? Could it be that the machinery itself is adding a contaminant?"

"I've got another question," Rick continued. "Because our soil here is low in magnesium, the forage we harvest is low in it too. So we asked that the batches of feed made up for our herd have magnesium oxide added to make up for this natural deficiency. Could someone at the feed plant have made a mistake and added *manganese* oxide instead? The chemical symbols are similar, after all."

"Absolutely not," Dr. McKean responded.

Not yet satisfied, Rick called the manager of the feed plant that had prepared the pellets. "Paul, I'd like to know what lubricant you're using on your pelleting machine."

"They're approved for this use," he responded. "Why do you ask?"

"Well, we're having an appetite problem with our cattle, and the source of it may be the #402 pellets you delivered a few days ago. In the 1940s and 1950s there was a mysterious disease in cattle called X Disease. Somebody noticed some animals who showed signs of the disease licking the grease off a feeder truck. Tests on the cattle for chlorinated naphthalenes, which are found in machine lubricants, came out positive. But a second source of lubricant had also contaminated the feed itself—and that was from the pelleting machine. Since then the USDA has controlled all lubricants used in feed equipment."

"We follow those regulations, Rick. You can be sure nothing like that happened here."

"How about the magnesium oxide? Where does it come from?"

"Michigan Chemical Company of St. Louis. I can assure you it's pure: it's the same stuff they use in antacid tablets for humans."

Rick knew the name Michigan Chemical Company. They also made the salt blocks they used for the cattle. "We also requested that the feed have added copper and zinc—twice as much as you normally put in this formula. Could the mixer have made an error in doing this?"

"No. We didn't add the separate salts you requested, because our supply of them doesn't come that way. All of the trace minerals are sent pre-mixed, so to increase the copper and zinc, we just added more of the pre-mix. Only calcium, phosphorus, and magnesium are added from separate bags."

"Might the corn have been moldy?" Rick went on.

"No. All the corn we've used at the feed plant this year has come from government stocks. It wasn't harvested last year."

Rich apologized for grilling the plant manager at such length, but he was impressed by the straightforward answers he had received. Still, there were some nagging questions, and he resolved to do more reading in his veterinary texts when he got home.

Most of that evening he spent stretched out on the sofa. The noise of Stephanie, Kristen, and Lisa playing on the carpet in front of him did not reach him: he was lost in a dizzying world **17** of symptoms. Each new heading was a voyage of discovery, possibly the beginning of the answer to the baffling production loss. The children went to bed unnoticed. It was after midnight when the words began to slip from his mind as he read them.

3

THE MORNING SUN slanted across the black strip of
road, leaving streamers of light in its path and dashes of
shadow where it dodged around the sugar maples. Every humble weed and blade of grass had its own share of the fire. I
remembered a morning like this when the glory of the new day
had made me take to the car with my camera, looking for
something ordinary that had been made glorious by the light.
No such luxury today: the children would soon begin their
procession down the stairs—Stephanie sliding down on her
backside, followed by Kristen in the more conventional way,
but looking more asleep than awake. Later, when we had eaten
our breakfast, Lisa would call out from her crib, and the day
would begin in earnest.

Every sunrise was different, it seemed to me after watching
hundreds of them, but none of them lasted. In less than an hour
the sun would be too high to cast the brilliant spikes of light
that ran along the edges of everything. But finding a few quiet
moments to watch it before the busyness of the day was one of
the joys of farm living that would probably have been difficult
to explain to acquaintances who wondered why we had given
up the conveniences and comforts of city life.

As I did battle with the dust whose presence the morning
sun highlighted, I thought about Rick and what the day might
bring for us. He had been heartened by the readiness of the
Agriculture Department veterinarians whom Dr. Jackson had

called to add their expertise to the investigation. With their wider contacts they would perhaps have a clue to the cows' loss of appetite. As time passed, and production continued to drop, it became less and less likely that this was "just one of those things" that would take care of itself.

I knew that Rick was worried about the cows, but he was also concerned because this was the time of year when the "base" or quota for next year's production was set. Our hopes of matching last year's high quota were virtually gone. If we did solve the problem soon, it could well mean that next year we would still have to sell any milk we produced over the virtual trickle that the cows were now yielding at much lower "surplus" prices. I tried to dismiss the thought of that kind of financial blow from my mind and concentrate on the more immediate responsibilities of the day ahead.

It was shortly after ten o'clock when Rick looked up from his desk in the milkhouse to see the two state veterinarians arrive in the familiar pea-soup green car with the state seal on the side. As they were slipping into their coveralls and preparing their sampling paraphernalia, Dr. Jackson also drove up.

"What do you think we've got here, Ted?" Dr. Carter asked Dr. Jackson as they moved toward the gleaming stainless steel washing tank in the milkhouse.

"I'm stumped," Dr. Jackson admitted. "It looks like an outbreak of IBR, but there are no temperatures. There's almost universal lacrimation in one barn. All of the animals are refusing their feed, and production is way down."

"Our milk shipments are down nearly thirty percent and still dropping 400 pounds a day," Rick interjected.

Dr. Grover gave a low whistle. "I can see why you're concerned—it couldn't happen at a worse time of year, could it? Well, let's get started."

"I have some of the most affected individuals isolated in the box stalls," Rick offered. "Maybe you'd like to look at them first." The four men made their way the length of the holding area that bisected the two barns, chatting amiably about the cattle-handling devices on the farm, which had been designed by Karl Halbert, Rick's second cousin and one of our hired men who was always building novel devices to help with the farm work. As they reached the newest barn, Rick pointed the three veterinarians to the box stalls, where he had penned up several of the high-producing cows with the tearing eyes.

"Couldn't miss these symptoms," Dr. Grover said. "Just look at those eyes!" He set down his container of sample bottles and watched the cows in the stall beside him. "But they don't seem to be breathing rapidly," he added. "Let's take a closer look."

He pointed out a young cow to Rick, who entered the stall and put the animal's head in the catching stanchion at the end of the stall. "How long have these animals been like this?"

"About a week." Dr. Jackson looked toward Rick, who nodded in agreement.

Dr. Carter brought the sampling kits to the cow's head, and Rick held the cow while the doctor carefully probed deep into her nostrils with the cotton-tipped swab. The three took swab samples from all of the cows Rick had penned up, carefully putting each swab into its own sealed container and labeling it. Dr. Carter wrote the tested cow's tag number on each of the test-tube-like sample bottles as he sealed them.

"Do you think it's a virus?" Dr. Jackson asked Dr. Grover.

"Well, it's possible. Let's take some temperatures while the cattle are relatively subdued."

Dr. Carter recorded the cows' temperatures in a notebook and also on the sample tubes. Glancing back at his notebook when they had finished, he remarked, "There's nothing unusual here—they're virtually normal. But the manure does look awfully pasty."

"About how much feed are they consuming now?" Dr. Grover turned to Rick, who had just freed the last animal they had sampled.

"Typically very little of the parlor feed—some of the cows won't even look at it. The milkers say that the cows just stand at the milking stations with their heads in the air. Judging from the drop in outside feed consumption, I'd say that our average cow is consuming about half her normal ration there."

"No wonder you're worried. I can't see how those animals could produce for very long if they're not eating. Can we take a look at your feed?"

Rick led them to a manger and scooped his hands through

the corn silage spread out in it. "This is the current silage ration."

Dr. Grover took some of the spicy and pungent silage in his hands and smelled it; then he ran a stream of the fermented material though his fingers into the other hand, alert for any unusual coloring or smell. "Everything seems normal here, not spoiled or moldy." Dr. Carter, who had also taken a handful, agreed.

"Are you using a topdressing?" Dr. Grover asked.

"We bought some high-moisture corn from a neighbor for topdressing," Rick said. As they walked through the milking parlor on the way back from the barns, Dr. Carter took a handful of the #402 pellets from one of the feed cups and rolled it between his hands. Finding nothing unusual, he dropped the pellets back into the next feed cup he passed. As they were cleaning up at the washing tank, Dr. Grover said, "It should be about a week before these samples can tell us anything. We'll have to let the cultures grow before we read them." Turning to Dr. Jackson, he added, "Call us in about a week, Ted, and we should have the results for you. This is probably a virus of some sort. It is still warm enough outside for flies to transmit disease from cow to cow." Dr. Carter had relit his ever-present pipe, and was beginning to take the rack of samples out to the car.

Dr. Grover looked around the milkhouse for any stray pieces of their veterinary equipment. "You've done a good job in putting this setup together and making it work. This little virus—or whatever it is—should be something we can help you get over in a week or so."

As Dr. Grover was putting the last bag of supplies in the trunk of the state car, Rick added, "We're planning to have samples of the feed tested this week for nitrates and excess urea. I've also requested that a dairy nutritionist come down from Michigan State and go through our feeding program to see if something is wrong with the nutrition in the cows' diet."

"Good. You might as well touch all of the bases," Dr. Grover replied as he slipped his jacket on his tall, cowboy-like frame.

"I also notified Farm Bureau shortly after the whole thing began. I thought they should know in case something's wrong with the pelleted feed." Then he added, almost as an after-thought, "If you happen to see someone else who has the same set of problems, let me know. I'd sure like to know what this is and how to get over it."

"We will—though you're the only ones who have come up with this so far," Dr. Grover said as he climbed into the car.

I could sense beneath Rick's worries an underlying determination to master the challenge the production drop had presented us. "Touching all the bases," as Dr. Grover had said, seemed the most natural course; and along with the discouragement of watching the cows suffer and production drop there was the fascination of pursuing the problem—not as though it were a problem in a college chemistry lab but as a matter of economic survival.

While waiting for the swab culture results, Rick had prepared feed samples for lab testing in Kalamazoo. The likeliest source of the problem, he realized, was what they ate most: the corn silage. If the laboratory testing disclosed a problem with urea content or nitrates or something else that escaped the nose and the naked eye, it might mean dumping $250,000 worth of silage—enough to last until next summer. To these tons of feed two thousand man hours of work had been contributed—long days of planting, cultivating, and harvesting—and I knew that if it had to go unused the loss would not only be a financial one, but a blow to the spirit of the men who lived close to the land.

"Don Hillman stopped by this morning," Rick told me at lunch the next day.

"The nutrition specialist?"

"Right. He read through the nutrition statement supplied with the pelleted feed and said it sounded good to him."

"Well, what does he think the problem is then?"

"He wants us to stop using that topdressing of high-moisture corn. There's a crust of mold on it just from last week's rain. He took a sample of it to test, but I'd already decided to take it out to the field with the manure spreader; and we haven't fed any of that corn since it got wet anyway."

"How about the silage itself?" I asked.

"Well, he took various samples from the silo for testing. But he thinks we should take all the cows off their regular feed immediately, except for the young stock. So we're going to try feeding them dry hay for a while."

Early the next morning Rick, his father, and his brother Mark assembled in the small barn office to go over the day's work assignments with the hired men. Sorting through the notes he had already made that morning, Rick began, "We're going to try something different with the cows. Most of you saw Don Hillman here yesterday; he suggested that we put the cows on dry hay and green chop until we find out what is wrong. Last night Gordon began feeding the dry hay. Today we're going to get the mower and chopper out of the barn and get them ready for chopping again. Gordon, you're going to be getting the mower ready. Jim and Karl can feed the cows dry hay. Mark, you'll be feeding calves and young stock. Nile and John will do the afternoon milking. Dad will start cutting hay."

"On the Dixon farm," the older man interjected. "That's where the alfalfa is best. I think we can get the most out of that field."

"What's wrong with the regular feed?" Jim asked. "Did Hillman have any idea why the cows won't eat it?"

"We don't know yet. The feed has been sampled and sent to the laboratory," Rick replied. "Until we *know* there's nothing wrong with it, we won't give it to the cows. Something seems to have upset their digestion. Now if the feed doesn't bother the young stock, we'll continue to give it to them, but I want anyone who feeds them to watch closely for any of those same symptoms in the young animals: loss of appetite, tearing."

By noon Gordon had the knives on the haybine sharpened and the machine ready for the field. Rick's father took the odd-looking contraption down the lane toward the Dixon place. Of all the men, he was most accustomed to the lever steering and peculiar balance problems of this strange self-propelled device, with its widespread wheels in front and two closely spaced wheels in back for maneuverability in tight places. While he cut and windrowed the hay with the haybine, Gordon pulled the chopper out of the barn, sharpened its cutting knives, and greased it. After the hay had been cut, Gordon pulled the chopper into the field with the tractor, and began to reduce the green hay to small pieces about as long as grass clippings. The chopped hay was then blown into a large farm truck, which hauled it back to the waiting cattle.

Back at the barn, Rick watched apprehensively as the feeder truck brought in the first load, pouring the fresh green hay onto the cement feed apron alongside the barn. How would the cattle act when presented with the new feed? The cows crowded up to the feeder. Rick felt a catch in his throat; they were going at the green hay as if they hadn't eaten in a lifetime! The scene was repeated in all of the barns, and the cows were voraciously hungry. Rick ran to the next truck that came into the driveway: "Tell Gordon to chop another round! They've eaten everything we've given them!" As Karl pulled out with the message, Rick felt better than he had in days. We had begun to turn the corner at last!

Our elation was to be short-lived, however. For four days, the cows did well on the all-hay regimen. The milk production began to edge upward. Rick and his father discussed the possibility of reintroducing the #402 pellets as parlor feed. After talking it over, they decided to see what would happen. The first day, the cows ate the pellets as though they had never suffered any appetite loss at all. But by the second day they began to ignore the pelleted feed again, and their milk production started to drop.

"That's it!" Rick said to his father. "No more of that stuff. I'm turning the controller off." The older man's face betrayed his disappointment; he had assumed the problem was solved when the cows had gone on the all-hay diet. "What can we put in the parlor feed cups to keep them occupied during milking?" Rick wondered. "Not having anything there is just asking for problems with their behavior."

"How about molasses blocks," Ted suggested. "A cow could keep pretty busy licking one of those while being milked. You know, I think whatever we do we'd better take those #402 pellets out of the bulk feeder tank in case there is something wrong with them. As long as they are in there, it's just too easy to turn the feeder back on, and the whole problem might start back up again. Karl and I can take care of emptying the tank one of these days."

After a week of feeding the cows nothing but hay, Rick

decided to balance their diet somewhat by adding ground oats, ground corn, and soybean meal. In case Don Hillman's suspicions about the moldy corn were on target, there might be a threat of liver damage in the cows, so he added some tetracycline and fat-soluble vitamins to the regimen as well. To help improve rumen activity, he added a small amount of cobalt chloride to the water tanks. By mid-October their condition had stabilized, but milk production had hardly improved.

Rick's father and Karl had unloaded the bulk feeder tank and dumped seven tons of the #402 pellets on the floor of the haymow in the large barn at Rick's father's place. The cone-shaped base of the feeder was difficult to empty, so Karl climbed inside the tank and shoveled the remaining ton of pellets into bags. It was dusty work, and when they had finished, there were twenty 80-pound burlap bags of the pellets.

"Let's put those bags in the yearling barn," Rick's father **25** suggested. "If the cows won't eat them, maybe we can feed them to the yearlings."

The laboratory reports were now beginning to come in. The state veterinarians reported that the cows did not have IBR or any other identifiable infectious disease. The tests by the private laboratory in Kalamazoo indicated no excessive urea content or nitrates in the feed. Don Hillman's report on the high-moisture corn revealed that the organisms present in the moldy-looking pile had only been yeasts. Since the findings of both tests were negative, and the cows' appetites were improving, Rick and Ted decided to reintroduce the corn silage into their diet. They combined it with the last of the fresh hay, which was running out.

What was the problem? The cattle were not infected; their food was not contaminated. What had gone wrong? As Rick sat with Don Hillman's report in front of him, Gordon walked into the office. He had just fed the young stock, and as a long-term employee Rick respected his judgment. "Have you seen anything unusual with the cows? Are they still eating the silage?"

"They're eating normally as far as I can tell. The early feeding is all gone when I bring the second one to them." He paused for a moment, and then added, "All the young stock is eating normally—except for the yearlings in the pink barn. I don't think we should keep giving those pellets to them."

"What pellets?" Rick looked up from the papers on his desk.

"Your Dad and Karl bagged some of the pellets that were in the bulk feeder and put them in the pink barn and told me to feed them to the yearlings until they were used up. I've been feeding them ever since—but now the animals are acting peculiar."

"How long have you been feeding them?"

"About a week."

"Do you have any left?"

"Only a hundred pounds or so."

"Okay. Stop feeding the calves those pellets and put them back on their regular feed."

After he had finished talking with Gordon, Rick drove to the calf barn at his father's place. Here his brother Mark, accompanied by an entourage of barn cats, spent most of his day feeding and caring for the youngest calves. As Rick stepped into the nursery, he was greeted by a chorus of bawling: the calves regarded any human as their friend and dinner ticket. Mark was at the far end of the barn, his hands full of nursing bottles in their wire racks, and the cats underfoot. As Rick waited for his brother to finish, he scratched the coat of the calf in the pen nearest him. The animal seemed very tame; it did not shy away from his hand and seemed to appreciate being scratched behind the ears.

"Looks like you're raising a barnful of pets," he called to Mark.

Mark grinned. "At least they won't be wild in the parlor like those last heifers you bought."

"How many weanlings do you have in the vacant bull pens?" For a month or so the weaned calves had outnumbered the spaces available in the regular calf pens. Many of the cows were calving just in time to help boost their now-pathetic milk output.

"We've got twelve calves back there now," Mark said.

"Let's take a look at them. There's an experiment I want you to do for me." The two brothers walked out of the barn, up the sloping driveway to the bull pens, which were in a shed attached to the back of the barn. Opening the shed door, they descended a flight of stairs until they were facing the three bull pens. In the first pen stood a young breeding-age Holstein bull borrowed from the county sire-proving association. The farmers in the association hoped to prove the genetic superiority of the bulls they raised, and so loaned the animals to association members who needed a bull, hoping to find an unusually good sire who would beget the number of progeny needed to prove his ability to pass on his desirable traits. The bull eyed them warily through the fence, planting his hoofs squarely in the floor of his pen, and snorting softly through his nose, his breath coming in steamy spurts in the chilly air.

The next two pens held the dozen weanling calves. "I want you to feed these calves the pellets we dumped on the barn floor. Don't give them hay or silage or grain. I want to see what happens. If the calves won't eat the pellets, we're going to call Farm Bureau again."

"If they stop eating, I'll tell you," Mark said. He reached **27** over the sides of the pen, and the calves came up to him, eyes shining with curiosity, and began to try to suck on his fingers.

On his way back to the pickup truck, Rick slid the heavy mow door open and looked at the mound of the pelleted feed. It had been so tempting to buy the expensive supplement in bulk that they had ordered tons of it. Walking up to the pile, he grabbed a handful from the center and walked out into the pale autumn sunlight. The pellets looked innocuous enough—they were fairly uniform and greenish in color. Almost idly, he rolled them between his hands—as if he expected somehow to feel in his fingers the reason for the mysterious loss of appetite in the dairy herd.

"It's got to be here!" he thought. But the pellets were in-scrutable. He pinched several between his fingers and tasted them, hoping for an answer—a bitter taste, something to explain why the cows refused their ration. But there was nothing unusual, just the familiar grain taste he'd known since childhood from sampling grain ripening in the fields or shelled corn as it came from the combine.

Standing in the cold, rolling the pellets from hand to hand, he could see that some of them looked as if they had been frosted with something; they were lighter on the outside than many of the others. He broke these open to discover that their color was merely an external phenomenon.

Every day when Rick came into the mow to check the grain bins for the calf barn below, he passed the mound of pellets and the question arose again: What is happening here? Could it be that, in spite of the careful controls and inspections at the plant, something had gotten into these pellets? He stooped to sample the pellets several times, each time from a different place in the mound, each time expecting to find something unusual. But the pellets told him nothing.

For the rest of the month, the mound of pellets brooded over the animals in the barn—innocent in appearance and taste, yet somehow not benign. He could not look at the cattle without suspicion. Each symptom became a lead to follow, each sick cow a bad omen.

4

A S NOVEMBER'S DAYS grew shorter and cooler, outdoor work on the farm slowed down. The worst of the feed crisis had apparently passed. The cows were eating again and seemed to be healthy, except for some rapid hoof growth and an unusual amount of lameness. The tearing had stopped. Milk production was stable, though at a level far below early September production, thus presenting a serious problem with the quota for next year.

The situation was taking its toll on all of us. Rick's determination to pursue the cause with the problem-solving skills he had learned in training to be an engineer could not entirely overcome the gnawing realization that the scientific tests done so far had yielded nothing. Once he even investigated the possibility that a disgruntled former hired hand might have poisoned the cows as an act of sabotage. The man had been hired at a busy time during the summer, and it was not until he had worked a few days that Rick had bothered to check his references. It was then that we learned of his chronic alcoholism and prison record for assault. Rick and his father had decided to keep him working, on the condition that he not operate machinery or show up at work inebriated.

Late in August, the man had taken his paycheck and driven to the local bar instead of home. Around midnight, Rick's father had found him, slumped drunkenly over the steering wheel, in the driveway. The next day he was fired.

The likeliest way to sabotage the cattle was to plant a chemical in the two-hundred-gallon water tanks in each barn. Methodically, Rick and his brother Mark emptied the tanks and scrubbed the interiors with the same cleansing solution they used on the bulk milk tanks. It was late in the afternoon when they got to the last one. As Mark began to drain it, he suddenly began laughing: "There's a goldfish in here!"

Rick grinned. One of the hired men had brought his children's goldfish to the water tank when it grew too large for its bowl. After washing and refilling all the tanks, they had found the proof that the water was not poisoned swimming around in the last tank!

There were other annoyances and worries adding to the tension—some of them obviously unrelated to the situation with the cows; some obviously related; and some that would leave us wondering in the months ahead. The cumulative effect made for a continuing uneasiness. A stab of pain woke me up one night to mark the beginning of a spreading kidney infection. Before that was taken care of, Lisa's cough had gotten worse instead of better, and what we thought was a common cold tracked home from kindergarten by her older sister turned out to be pneumonia and required ten days in the hospital in Battle Creek. Things fell into a quiet routine finally, but it was December before all of us were healthy again.

On a November Sunday afternoon while Rick was repairing the starter on one of the old farm trucks, he saw one of the hired men running toward him, obviously very agitated.

"The panel in the compressor room burned out!" Nile reported breathlessly. "We were cleaning up the milking parlor, Karl and I, and we smelled the kind of smoke you get with an electrical fire. I managed to put out the fire with the extinguisher, but the control panel is a mess!"

The burnt-out control panel, covered with the fine chemical dust from the extinguisher, was the master control for the entire barn complex. Through it ran the current that operated the waterers, the lights, the various pumps, most importantly at this moment the compressor and milk pump. There was no way to milk the four hundred cows by hand; and what milk they did get could not be kept fresh and cold until the hauler came.

"Call Whitney," Rick said. "We need an electrician on the double. And see if you can get Consumers Power to help." When Karl had gone out to throw the main switch off so that Rick could begin to assess the damage, he had discovered that the current had blown the main fuse as well.

Whitney's assessment was quick and discouraging. "There's no way to get that thing working without replacing the whole panel. And I don't have anything like that in my shop. I can do the installation all right, but it beats me where I can get a panel like that on Sunday."

Rick persuaded him to go look for one anyway. Meanwhile, he returned to the compressor room to see if there was any way to run the bare bones of the milking operation for the afternoon milking. With a chisel he began to chip away the carbon and the now-useless insulation. He figured that a third of the panel would be enough for this emergency; if they had to postpone the milking their already dismal production would be even further harmed.

Two hours later the junk bucket at his feet was piled with ruined circuit breakers, but the panel was beginning to yield some usable circuits. When Whitney returned to report that he had not been able to locate a suitable panel, he was surprised to see the old one, which he had given up as a lost cause, limping along well enough for the afternoon milking to start. The problem with the electrical control panel had briefly taxed Rick's ingenuity, but he had met the challenge with improvisation under pressure, and had succeeded—unlike the problem with the cows, which was not responding to his efforts at a solution.

Less than a week later Rick walked into the compressor room shortly after midnight to pull his rubber barn boots on and to check the new control panel Whitney had installed to replace the makeshift arrangement. Convinced that everything was in order, he went on into the milking parlor to begin setting out the milkers. In a few minutes Nile would join him; the first cows would come into the holding area; and the midnight milking would begin.

Rick and Nile milked together on the weekends while the regular milking teams rested. Milking was a rhythmic six-hour job, usually uneventful unless punctuated by a threatening uplifted hoof or a heifer that forgot how to enter the parlor and got herself in backwards. The men exchanged small talk or listened to the radio.

Each man milked eight cows—four on each side of the parlor pit. After the cows had entered the parlor and had begun to work on the feed in the feed cups, the milkers would wash their udders, massage them to start the milk flowing, and then attach the automatic milking machine. By the time that a milker finished the last cow in his string, the first cow might be through being milked. If her milker showed no more of the white fluid in the clear piping at its base, it would be removed and washed. Each of the cow's teats would be dipped in a medicated solution to help ward off infection while the milk canals were open. When all the cows had been milked, one man would leave to begin cleaning the barns with a small tractor, while the other would clean the milking parlor and put away the milkers on a large metal rack to be rolled into the milkhouse for washing and storing.

On this particular morning, Rick was cleaning the parlor. As he was attaching the rack of milkers to the automatic cleaning system, Karl walked into the milkhouse to ask about his morning work assignment.

"Have you seen those two rats in the milkhouse lately?" Rick asked Karl. "I just realized that I haven't seen a mouse or rat here for several days." Karl had a special interest in the rats in the milkhouse, since it usually fell to him to fix the wiring that the rodents had a penchant for chewing through. Since the weather had grown colder, he had had to make such repairs several times, in spite of the generous supplies of rat poison he had placed in every corner. In fact, the rats seemed to thrive on the poison.

"No, I haven't seen any rats for over a week," Karl replied. "But it's not because of the poison; I've given up on that."

"Well," said Rick, "maybe your worries about the wiring are over. I'm going back to the house for a nap. I'll be back after lunch." He climbed in his pickup and drove off. The sudden absence of rats was intriguing.

Postponing the nap he usually took after a turn of morning milking, he turned the truck in at his Dad's place to ask Mark if he had seen any rats around the milkhouse recently, since Mark was in and out of that building all day getting milk for the calves. He found Mark up to his elbows in the milk replacer he was mixing in the calf barn. "Remember those rats that ate the wiring in the milkhouse? Have you seen them around recently?"

Mark looked up from the frothy white brew. "No, I haven't seen them." Then he added somewhat sadly, "I haven't seen any of my cats here either—not even the white one. I've put milk out for them the last two or three days and they haven't shown up to drink it."

"Maybe something has killed the rats off. Maybe there's a disease rampant in their population. Have you ever seen a farm with no rats?"

Mark went back to mixing the milk replacer for the calves, then he stopped and looked up at Rick. "I almost forgot to tell you—the bull pen calves won't eat the pellets any more. What do you want me to do with them?"

"Try giving them some silage with the pellets as a top-dressing and keep me posted. Right now, I'm going home for a nap. I'll be back to breed heifers this afternoon."

On the way home, Rick reflected on the disappearance of the milkhouse rats and the barn cats. He had always taken them for granted. The rats gave him a headache in the grain storage areas and, lately, in the milkhouse; but like most farmers he had long ago concluded that rats were an irritating inevitability of life on the farm. Baited, trapped, poisoned, they persisted nonetheless, almost admirable in their cleverness at avoiding man's snares. The idea that some kind of disease was raging through their colony was not completely satisfying. Their disappearance seemed too sudden. No one had seen a single tottering rat going after the stray grains of feed in the milking parlor. One day, the rats simply disappeared. What lethal agent had whisked them away?

As Rick ate his lunch, I could sense that something was really bothering him. He told me what he had learned about the disappearance of the small animals. The calf barn, he reflected aloud, was over a mile and a half from the milking parlor. If the barn cats had been able to eat the parlor rats, he could have rationalized the disappearance of both more easily. But he didn't think the two populations overlapped. Was there some general disease that had wiped them out? His lunch finished, Rick left for the barn, giving up his nap.

I was saddened at the loss of the barn cats, though I knew how they got underfoot and tended to overpopulate the barn. Still, they had a right to live on the place, and they did a valuable job in rodent control. Besides, I liked to see the sinuous animals stalk and leap and rest in a sunny windowsill. They were the few survivors of city pets grown inconvenient to their owners and left at the roadside. Most cats thus abandoned did not survive the cruel ribbon of road or the commuters' daily race to work and then back. Some succumbed to the big farm dogs, which had no liking for the smaller predators. The few survivors had to find their own way, had to learn to be feral cats again. Their bodies sleeked down, they lived as shadows in the mow and the granary of the big barn. Calicos, tigers, and an occasional longhair would slink along the walls, sun themselves, and dash off in wild fear at the merest hint of a sudden human interruption. The children didn't understand how long it took to tame the barn cats—Uncle Mark, after all, walked around with one on his shoulders—and ran after them with well-intentioned fistfuls of "cat food," trying to make friends.

In spite of their furtive ways, the cats fit in. Now there were no more cats.

A few days later Rick was in his office in the barn, where he tried for the hundredth time to make sense of what was happening to him and to the farm. He reached for the pile of health records, shook off the sleepiness enveloping him, and began paging through them. Without looking up when Mark walked in, he said to his younger brother, "There are four cows for you to breed in the third barn."

"Four more!" Mark exclaimed. "I thought I was finished." He dropped onto the corner of the desk with a sigh. "Have you noticed how many of the cows are showing up on the breeding list? How many did you breed yesterday?"

"Ten. Every time I thought I was finished, somebody seemed to have added one or two to the list in there. I spent most of my time running back here to get more semen out of the jug."

"You know," Mark said, "I'm sure that I've bred two cows

today that I bred and pregnancy-checked a couple weeks ago. Something strange is going on. I'm sure that Pee Wee was on the list as settled, but here she is on the breeding list again."

Rick put the health records back into the file. "Let's go see how the cows are acting. Something must be happening to the embryos. Have you seen any sign that they're aborting?"

"No," Mark replied, opening the large metal jug of bull semen that was in the corner beside the desk and pulling a long, thin glass tube out of the churning mist of the liquid nitrogen, $-320°$ F, which kept it preserved. "I'm not going to use that twenty-five-dollar bull on these cows... even at ten bucks a service we're spending a lot on breeding if they don't settle."

Artificial insemination had been used on the Halbert farm for twenty years. Rick's father had watched his herd of Holsteins improve five percent in milk production with each genera- **35** tion of breeding an ordinary cow with a superior bull. He had never liked keeping a mature bull; he knew too many men who had had their bulls turn on them, and a few had not lived through the encounter. They kept only a young bull for the heifers now, selling him as soon as he began to show signs of aggressive behavior—pawing the concrete floor of the barn as a man entered the lot, gazing too steadily, herding the cows behind him at the approach of a man. A full-grown dairy bull was a magnificent animal to behold—from a distance.

To keep up, Rick and Mark took turns artificially breeding the cows now. The job was a necessary one if the cows were to continue their yearly calving cycle. Equipped with a glass ampule of bull semen, a hypodermic syringe, a plastic catheter, and a disposable plastic glove-and-sleeve combination that reached up to one's shoulder, Mark set out for the third barn. Taking the extra ampules of semen in a cup of ice water, Rick followed him through the parlor and into the holding area. As they walked, they both watched the cows in the lots next to the holding area, looking for the telltale signs that the cows were in heat.

A cow ready for breeding will invite other cows to mount her if there is no bull in the lot. Anyone in the barn when an animal showed this behavior was to write down the number of the animal on the list of cows ready to be bred. If they did not catch a cow when she was ready for breeding, it meant an expensive wait of three weeks until she would cycle back again. The cows were bred eight weeks after calving, and carried an unborn calf for nine months while they were also in milk. Two months before the birth of her calf, she would be dried up—that is, they would stop milking her, allowing her to recuperate before her calf was born. With each birth, the cycle of breeding-back and milk production began anew.

Later in the week, as Rick was making his daily rounds to check the grain for the calves, he came into the mow of the big barn. Before him lay the last of the pellets, the green mound scooped out on one side by Mark's shovel to feed the twelve calves in the experiment. Since it was early in the day, the calves had not been fed yet; and they had bawled up at him as he had passed their pen. So far, there was no change in their behavior, except that they would not eat the pellets anymore. But there was little indication of the tearing seen in the cows. Walking slowly by the pile, Rick started at something that lay directly in his path. There were two cats stretched out near the pile of pellets. One of them was Mark's white cat. Rick knelt to examine the cats, which were both stiff. There was no indication of a violent death, no marks of a fight with the big German shepherd that often killed the slower or less wary barn cats.

Rick was mystified. It was unusual to see one dead cat, let alone two, which had apparently succumbed to the same nameless thing about the same time. Sometimes the workers would find the dried-up corpse of an ancient barn cat when they cleaned out the tool shed, but usually sick cats crept off by themselves to die somewhere, preferring to meet their end in solitude. There was no evidence that these cats had been diseased—their body condition appeared to be good; there were no crusted eyes or nose on either cat.

On his way home, Rick decided to stop at the barn to see if anyone had fed the cows yet. When he had had the chance lately, he fed them himself: he wanted to ascertain whether their appetites had truly returned. As he walked into the parlor, he could see that the usually calm Nile was quite agitated. "Am I glad to see you, Rick. There's a cow out in the maternity stall that's having some trouble calving."

Eighty-five percent of the calves born on the farm were born without the help of man. Still, to try to improve the mortality rate of both cow and calf, all of the men watched the dry cows for the familiar signs of impending delivery: developing an udder full of milk and a mucus-like vaginal discharge. Such a cow would be placed in one of the large, straw-bedded maternity stalls at the end of the lot where she could be watched by anyone walking through the holding area. Usually, the labor and delivery of a normally presenting calf, with its front hoofs bracketing its nose, took no more than four hours. If the presentation was wrong, or if the labor was too long, Ted, Rick, Mark, Nile or Gordon would be called in to assess the situation. In most of the more difficult cases, rotating the calf or attaching obstetrical chains to its front hoofs and pulling with each contraction of the cow's uterus would result in a smoother birth. The few really difficult deliveries required the assistance of Dr. Jackson.

Learning that this cow, which was two weeks past her calving date, had been straining for an unusually long time, Rick put aside all thought of feeding the cows and trotted to the maternity stall. Calf-puller in hand, he hurried over to the cow, stretched out on her side in the large, straw-bedded stall. He could see that she was nearly overcome by fatigue. Her contractions were weak, and her neck was stretched out. She was breathing rapidly and shallowly, uttering an occasional loud moan. The strange, strained lowing of the laboring cow echoed through the barn; but indifferent to her predicament, the other cattle in the barn carried on their daily routine.

Rick realized that if the cow strained much longer without delivering, she would probably become paralyzed by the constant nerve-pinching trauma. Obviously, the calf was too large and the head seemed to be caught in the cow's birth canal. Rick could see only the forefeet and the nose of the calf, but the cow seemed to be making no progress. He had waited long enough; it was time to assist the delivery.

Attaching the obstetrical chains to the calf's protruding forefeet, Rick hooked the small hand-operated winch to a post ten feet away. He applied the tension slowly, expecting the cow to respond with strong contractions; she should be straining every ten seconds or so. After several strong contractions, the calf began to move slowly. Finally, the whole head emerged, and Rick sighed with relief.

When the calf had moved a foot or so more, progress halted. Rick had seen this happen before; it was usually a brief respite before the final pushes. But the longer the calf did not move the more Rick felt a building sense of urgency. The unborn calf's navel had now passed into the cow's cervix, pinching it. If it stayed in this position much longer it would suffocate. Struggling against an invisible life clock, he tried to do what could not be done; the calf was caught firmly by its hips in its dam's pelvis. Rick swore violently at his own powerlessness as he tried to turn the unborn calf; somehow he must find the combination that would free it.

The calf gasped desperately like a fish out of water, but it could not expand its lungs. Rick tried rotating the calf 180° in both directions, loosening the winch repeatedly. The calf should have been taken by Caesarean section, but it was too late. Its eyes took on a disquieting stare; then it stopped gasping.

The moment the frantic struggle to save the calf was over, a new struggle began: saving the exhausted, defeated cow. Rick ran back to the barn office and looked for a knife; the only one he could find was the pocket knife in the veterinary supply box. He felt the blade and gave a small prayer of thanks—it was very sharp. On the way back to the maternity stall, he grabbed a long rubber milking apron, a bucket, and some soap; things must be kept as clean as possible. Returning to the barn, he realized, was his only choice, though he dreaded it. Calling the veterinarian would mean at least an hour's wait—if he was not already out on a call somewhere else.

The cow remained stretched out on her side; Rick hoped that her spirit was still strong. Laying the rubber apron beneath the half-presented calf, he shuddered at the touch of cold, wet death: it was a sensation to which he could not get accustomed, though he had handled it many times before.

The only way to remove the calf was backwards—but it was impossible to push the calf back into the cow's uterus. His only hope for success was to cut the dead calf in half and try to manipulate the half that was stuck. Grasping the knife firmly, he cut through the abdomen and the supple bones of the rib cage. The calf's blood covered his hands and arms; the mother lay motionless as part of her offspring dropped to the straw. As Rick pulled the front half of the calf away from the exhausted cow, he was struck by the ghastly, surreal scene in which he was an actor. With his bloody hands, he zipped open his coveralls and dropped them to his waist; then, he went to the bucket and scrubbed up. Dropping to his knees behind the cow, he pushed on the stump of the calf's spine; it moved easily back toward the cow's uterus. Its sharpness worried him, for it could easily puncture the thin lining of the uterus and cause peritonitis and probably death.

He had returned almost all of the calf's hindquarters to the uterus when the cow began to strain. "Not now!" he cried. His arms were nearly numb from pushing against the cow. "Relax. Please relax." Shortly, she seemed to sense that there would be no progress. Her muscles slackened, and Rick was able to remove one arm now that his first goal had been reached. The next step was to begin carefully turning the severed hindquarters in the cow's uterus.

"If only my arms were longer!" Rick thought. Blood was running down his arms to his shoulders and onto his chest. Now he found a rear foot, and was pushing it to the cow's cervix. A moment of searching, and he found the other leg. Then he discovered that he couldn't control both feet with one hand. Groping for the lost foot, he attempted to catch it with one of the obstetrical chains, but the chain on the foot caused too much tension. He tied the foot to the winch and concentrated on the second foot. With both hands on the easily lost foot, he pulled and guided it into place.

An hour had passed since Rick had begun to dissect the calf. He stood up and took several deep breaths. His arms were shaking and numb with fatigue; after flexing them to restore circulation, he stooped again.

Now was the moment of truth. He attached both feet to the winch and tightened until something should have happened—but nothing did happen. He tightened the winch again. This time, he noticed that the whole 1400-pound cow was slowly being pulled backward. He stopped pulling and considered tying her head to another post. In desperation, he tightened the winch again. To his relief, the calf's rear quarters began to slide from the birth canal.

The dissected calf delivered, Rick, covered from his chin to his knees with the blood of the sacrificed calf, stood up. With his coveralls still flapping from his waist, he walked back to the veterinary supply shelf and got a bottle of dextrose for the cow. He had to lessen the chance of shock and replace some of the fluids she had lost. He prepared an intravenous puncture of her jugular vein and gave her the dextrose solution; everything that was possible should be done, but her chance for surviving the ordeal was much in doubt.

When the dextrose was finished, Rick walked behind the exhausted cow and yelled, slapped her flanks, and succeeded in getting her at least to lie in a more upright position. Pushing straw bales next to her, he satisfied himself that she could not stretch out on her side again and die of bloat. Finally, he prepared a dose of antibiotic and gave it to her, praying that she would be able to fight the infection that would almost surely result from her trauma.

He began to move his tools from the stall and to clean the bloody straw from the place where he had first laid the dead calf. When he walked to the milkhouse for the last time, he noticed that night was falling; he would feel no sense of triumph at the close of this day.

One November afternoon I put a roast in the oven, slipped off my shoes, and stretched out on the couch in the living room for a short nap. In the past few weeks I had found that I needed a brief nap to get through the day. A clatter at the back of the house woke me with a start. Stephanie was at school, and the other two girls were sleeping upstairs. Before I could get out of the living room to check the noise Rick appeared at the door. Vaguely embarrassed at having been caught sleeping (though Rick had never complained about my taking a nap) and surprised to see him home in the middle of the afternoon, I asked him why he had missed lunch.

"We took delivery of the #112 pellets today," he said. "I had to help the truckers unload and then get the sacks covered. With deer hunting we were running two men short, so it took longer than I thought it would."

"How much did you get?"

"A hundred tons—to fill our contract. It should last through December, at the rate we've been using pelleted feed. The way soybean meal prices have risen, I'm sure this was the best deal we could hope for. #112 doesn't have the protein of #402, but we can add things to build up our diet at the feeders. I ordered it without magnesium oxide, by the way, in case that was the problem with the last batch of #402." He paused. "I can't see how the feed plant could have messed up all their feed formulas—they probably just ruined a batch or two of #402, and we were the lucky ones who bought their mistake! If they have a serious problem with the #112 feed, there should be a lot of complaints—it's the most commonly-used dairy feed they sell."

Covered with dust, Rick looked as tired as I felt. "Why don't you take a shower if you're going to be home for a while, and I'll heat up the lunch you missed."

"It smells like you've got something cooking already," he said. "Why don't we have an early dinner when Stephanie gets home, and I'll make up for the lunch on my own. I'll go shower—why don't you finish your nap?"

"I thought you didn't notice. . . ."

"There's a wrinkle from the pillow stamped on your cheek."

But any hopes for a longer nap were short-lived. Kristen thumped down the stairs; Lisa was soon awake; and not long after that Stephanie returned to add the final touch to the after-school chaos.

Eventually dinner made its way to the table. As I sat down after filling Kristen's cup for the second time, I asked Rick a question that had been bothering me all afternoon: "Could anything be wrong with this meat, do you think? The steer was butchered at the end of October, after we'd had all of the problems with the cows. Could the steer have gotten whatever it was that bothered them?"

Rick looked up from his dinner. He had never questioned that the steer was healthy; they had hand-raised the animal from a calf for meat. Raised with a group of heifers at the pink barn, it had never been sick a day in its life. "I don't think there's any reason to worry," he said. "This steer was at Dad's farm, not at the milking setup. Besides, the cows have come around recently. Whatever bothered them may have passed. Our death rate is actually lower now than it has been: we've only lost one cow in the past two months."

"You don't think there's any chance the steer caught anything?" I persisted.

"No. He should be as clean as the day he was born."

Rick's confidence allayed my fears for the moment. But the fact remained: as long as we didn't know what the problem with the dairy cattle had been, we couldn't know for certain the extent of the problem either.

5

IT WAS NOW December: a light snow had fallen overnight, but the morning was clear and crisp. Rick, preoccupied and silent, had left for the barn early, scarcely having said a word. Dr. Grover had given him the name of a man near Coopersville, north of Grand Rapids, who had recently had some breeding problems with his dairy herd and lowered production. Rick had called the farmer last night, but the conversation had not been very enlightening. The man from Coopersville was an immigrant, spoke English with a heavy accent, and had not recalled the number of the Farm Bureau feed his cattle had eaten.

After Rick left, I bundled up the two oldest children, leaving Lisa, still weak from her bout with pneumonia, in the dining room to watch us from the picture window. While Stephanie and Kristen frolicked in the powdery snow, not knowing what to do with it, I shoveled the driveway, lost in thought, envious at how the girls could enjoy themselves, unaware of the growing fear that was troubling us.

Not that life on the farm had ever been the idyll we might have dreamed of when we made the decision to leave Midland. The farmhouse, dating from the 1880s, showed far more age than charm. It stood out from its surroundings on a small rise; the kitchen and back room, added on later, seemed to be stepping off the hill. Landscaping was nonexistent; eager builders had cleared the forest to get to the farmland with no thought of leaving even a windbreak. On winter nights the inquiring west wind would howl in the many corners of the house and though we reassured the children over and over that no ghosts lurked about, they still did not understand the noises.

For Rick the fertile rolling land, sculpted eons ago by passing glaciers, was enough to allow him to overlook the aesthetic defects of the house while stealing the odd hour here and there to repair the most telling flaws in its construction. A woodchuck running loose in the basement had been the tipoff that it was past time to patch the foundation mortar. The bitter cold of the kitchen floor in winter had drawn us, armed with staple guns and fat rolls of insulation, into the abyss of the crawl space under the kitchen, where we uncovered a mummified rat, piles of firewood, and an impressive collection of aging *National Enquirers* and *Police Gazettes*.

But if repairs such as these had made the place livable, it was a far cry from what I had wanted. The outside of the house had been rendered nondescript by a previous owner's attempt at modernization, which had stripped it of its Victorian "gingerbread" trim. We found the delicate pieces of handmade woodwork, cut up beyond salvage, in a woodpile behind the house when we moved in: the craftsmanship of an age gone by, now suitable for nothing but stoking fires. Only the false pilasters that ran up the outside corners of the weathered house and seven pairs of original shutters remained to give it any character. Inside, wood paneling nearly everywhere served to cover the defects of the aging plaster walls. The remodeling reflected fashions in decorating which I had seen in farm magazines from the late 1950s.

Stephanie and Kristen were sliding down the pile of snow I had taken out of the driveway. Neither of them would remember when the bulldozer had come to take away the rundown collection of small buildings that had skirted the rise where the house stood. We had lived here barely two weeks at the time; I had looked up from unpacking to see the Caterpillar D9 mowing down the rickety old garage. Then the operator had dug a huge pit to serve as the final resting place for all of the foundation stones of the basement barn, which had blown down in a tornado three years earlier.

Later we had discovered the rest of that barn, buried in clumps of grass in the field. The day of the first plowing, Rick and I had gone ahead of the tractor, searching for pieces of red barnwood that might otherwise have flattened the $600 tires of the tractor.

The most difficult loss to the bulldozer had been the picturesque lane, which had divided the fields and provided a direct link to the distant rough pasture and the pond. On the first warm day, after we moved in, the children and I had walked back there, admiring the hickory trees that bordered it and scaring up a complacent woodchuck whose burrow ended in the grassy bank at the edge of the path. Kristen had never seen a woodchuck before, and she ran after this one, coming surprisingly close to touching it before the animal decided that his small visitor was a bit too large and enthusiastic for a playmate. Several hundred yards farther, a doe heavy with her spring fawn leaped out of the grass before us and disappeared into the woods at the back of the farm. The final fascination of the walk had been discovering a garter snake sunning itself.

I smiled now at their enthusiasm for farm life—a zest for the outdoors and its creatures which I shared and which I welcomed in them. But I snapped out of my daydream—the recollection of Rick's conversation the night before cast a shadow over the sunny winter morning. The farmer in Coopersville had told Rick that he had ended up selling all his cows for hamburger. The state veterinarians had taken a look at the carcasses, the farmer had told Rick, and had seen nothing to prevent their being processed for meat except for a few "enlarged livers." But the farmer reported that someone from the processing plant had said that he had personally seen the livers of some of the cows and that they were as big as washtubs.

I returned the snow shovel to its place in the garage and called the girls to go into the house. Domestic chores made the morning pass quickly, and soon it was time for Stephanie to get ready for school and lunch to be set on the table. Above the clatter of the dishes and silverware, I heard her exclaim with delight when Rick's pickup pulled into the driveway. "Look! Daddy's bringing us a pet calf!"

"A pet calf?" I asked, listening as the door to the back room slammed and Rick pulled off his boots.

"We can put it in the garage and make a fence around the

apple trees so he can live there!" the other children chimed in happily. But when Rick opened the door to the kitchen I saw immediately on his face the all-too-familiar signs of strain and worry.

"Is that calf for us, Daddy?" Stephanie asked eagerly.

"No, Stephanie," he replied, barely able to look her in the eye, "this calf is too sick to make a good pet. I'm going to take it to a place where a lot of animal doctors can look at it to find out what's making it sick."

"Maybe we can have it for a pet when it's all better," Kristen ventured tentatively.

"What's wrong?" I asked Rick quietly, trying to ignore the disappointment of the children.

"These calves have been eating those #402 pellets, but lately they've lost their appetites, and nothing Mark does seems to be working. The one in the truck won't even touch the corn silage anymore, and Dr. Jackson suggests that we take it to the Diagnostic Lab at Michigan State to see what the vets there can find out."

What he did not say in front of the girls was that the test at MSU would be a post-mortem. The veterinarians there would end the calf's four months of life humanely; and perhaps the examination that followed would yield a clue to the secret of the starving cattle. The girls suspected nothing of this; what they knew about doctors at their age had to do with healing.

The calf was still alive when Rick left for Lansing. Countless trips back and forth to the state capital had taught him every curve and bump of the road, and in spite of his efforts to concentrate on the too-familiar scenery, he caught himself looking in the rear view mirror for the emaciated passenger hidden under the gunny sacks. Yet the innocence of the stricken calf, its utter helplessness when they had loaded it—head down, eyes sunken—into the truck that morning, had etched themselves into Rick's mind.

An hour's drive brought him to the concrete loading ramp at the diagnostic laboratory. A white-coated assistant emerged from the rear entrance of the fortress-like brick building; he was joined by another assistant, and the three of them moved the dying calf into a shiny, brilliantly lit tile-walled room that smelled strongly of antiseptic. They put the calf on a large animal-sized examining table.

Notified in advance that Rick would be coming, a couple of veterinarians appeared in the examining room immediately, and began to ask questions about the calf and its medical history. How long had it been sick? Had it been treated by a veterinarian? Had it been vaccinated for the usual diseases? Had it been getting enough to eat?

The veterinarians seemed surprised to hear Rick say that the calf had been getting its feed *ad libitum*, because, as one said, "it looks like it hasn't had a thing to eat in weeks."

"What have you been feeding it, Mr. Halbert?" the other veterinarian asked.

"Farm Bureau's #402 24% protein silage balancer," Rick answered, trying not to betray any discomfort at the rapid-fire questioning.

"Why were you feeding a calf that particular feed?" The doctor's expression changed to one of surprise—feeding a calf Farm Bureau #402 was an extravagance.

"We were having some difficulty getting our cows to eat #402, and their daily milk production collapsed. When we fed the separate elements of their diet one by one, this feed was the only element that seemed suspicious. All of the rest of the diet had been cleared of suspicion by trial and error on the farm. When we found that there seemed to be a connection between feeding FB #402 and loss of appetite, we decided to put a pen of calves on the feed to see how they reacted. This is the first calf to show a dramatic loss of appetite. It's refused not only the pelleted feed but everything else as well."

The doctor stared at the calf, and began to look over its body for external signs of disease. He ran his hands through its rough coat, and looked up at Rick. "What condition was this animal in before you began to run your feeding trial?"

"All the individuals in the pen seemed to be in perfect health."

"No recent evidence of pneumonia," the doctor pressed him. "No running noses, no temperatures?"

Rick squirmed. From a purely scientific point of view that was the one flaw in the feeding trial. There had not been an opportunity to check each calf ahead of time to make sure it was not carrying a disease. If just one of the calves in the pen had a contagious respiratory disease, his whole experiment would be open to question. "They all appeared to be in perfect health three weeks ago," he offered hesitantly.

"Bring me the wires," the veterinarian said to an assistant, who returned almost immediately with a split extension cord which had an alligator clip on each end. Rick was startled by macabre apparatus. The veterinarian asked the assistant to attach one clip to the calf's upper lip and one to the hide of its tail. He nodded; and the cord was plugged into a wall outlet. Rick flinched as the black and white calf twitched convulsively and then was still.

The cold and impersonal room fell still. The veterinarians bent over the dead calf, preparing it for the post-mortem. The laboratory assistant brought in a tray of scalpels, sample bottles, and clamps. How different from the post-mortems Dr. Jackson had done for them in the barn, Rick mused. He could picture the dedicated and passionate family veterinarian, slowed only slightly by the effects of a heart attack, his face outlined by the glaring halo of the mechanic's trouble light, as he bent over a dead cow, his boots mired in manure, trying to exact the secrets of life and death. In contrast, the diagnostic laboratory procedure, carried out without emotion in this sterile, hollow-sounding room, seemed almost mechanical.

"Why don't you step outside to the lobby, Mr. Halbert," the senior veterinarian suggested.

Despite thinking that there was a slight edge of insistence in the doctor's voice, Rick demurred. "No, I'd really like to see what the post-mortem might show in the calf's gross pathology, if you don't mind."

"No problem," the veterinarian nodded. "Anytime you want something explained, just ask."

The first step was opening the calf's abdomen and examining its stomachs and intestines. The younger man cut open the stomachs and put them on a table to go over the contents. Only a small amount of partially digested silage was in the rumen, and there was a large ulcer in the lining of the fourth, or true, stomach. The ulcer surprised Rick. "Isn't the ulcer unusual for a calf this age?" he asked.

"We don't often see an erosion of the lining in a calf this young," the veterinarian replied. "I guess you could call it unusual." He paused to look over the contents of the stomach. "How much has this animal been eating? There doesn't seem to be much here."

"For the past two weeks it seems to have had virtually nothing," Rick answered. "It ate from a common trough and manger, and shared its feed with eleven other calves, so it's a little hard to tell; but no one who's been around the pen when the feed was put in has seen this calf eating for about two weeks. And it showed no interest in its food for the last four days, when we put it in another pen by itself to watch it and try to treat it. Something irreversible seems to have happened to its digestive system."

A laboratory assistant wrote something down on a note pad as Rick spoke. "Look at this!" the senior vet called to the others from his work in the calf's quarters. "These kidneys are definitely inflamed. Did you see any reduction in the calf's urine output, Mr. Halbert?"

"No, it never showed any signs of kidney problems; there appeared to be no pain and we noticed no reduction in the amount of urine we cleaned out of the stall where it was by itself. We did notice something strange, though. Some of the calves in the experiment were grinding their teeth—clamping them together and making noises that would drive you right up a wall. This calf was one of the worst. I remember wondering if it should be tested for lead poisoning."

"Write that down," the veterinarian instructed his assistant. "That could be a sign of lead poisoning, or maybe just of pain. We might have a case of kidney disease here, or it could be a red herring—but we might as well touch all the bases."

They turned next to the calf's heart and lungs. "Almost no fat on the heart. The animal's external condition was certainly poor, so I guess we shouldn't be too surprised by this, but I haven't seen many animals with so little fat internally."

The taller doctor removed the heart and lungs and examined them closely. "No sign of lung problems—no enlargement of any of the cardiovascular system."

The younger vet was breaking into the hind leg now. Taking a sample of something from the rear joint, he smeared it on a slide, which he labeled and put in a plastic sleeve in a box. Then he took another slide sample from the calf's intestine.

"We can't say for sure, but the kidney may have been the problem. That would explain the tooth-grinding. The animal might have been in pain and ground its teeth. But we'll check for lead in the samples; there's always a chance it got into some paint. Do you have any painted surfaces in those bull pens?"

"No. The rails are unpainted, and the rest of the pen surfaces are metal—the standard commercial manger and gate combination."

"Do you have any painted surfaces on any of the calf pens in your calf barn—or wherever the calf was kept prior to the experiment?"

"No, the interior of the barn is new. We use raised metal stalls for the calves in the calf barn. There's no way that the calf could have gotten into any old paint."

50

Six of the twelve calves in the experiment followed the same pattern of refusing feed and digestive disruption. Four weeks into the experiment, Mark quit feeding the calves the high protein silage balancer and tried giving them whole milk. That seemed to restore their appetite, but restoring them to health was apparently impossible. Scanning his textbooks for the symptoms of various nutritional disorders, Rick pursued the idea that the feed was creating a lethal nutritional deficiency in the animals. Maybe the toxin was destroying Vitamin B-12 or stopping the production of amino acids in their livers or interfering with thyroid activity. But when he and Mark dosed the calves with various combinations of vitamins, amino acid pills, and minerals like zinc, chromium, and selenium, there was no discernible improvement.

The second week of December, the arrival of the official-looking envelope from the diagnostic laboratory at MSU renewed my hope. Surely this would be the explanation we were awaiting, the answer that would put an end to the plague that had struck the cows. I watched anxiously as Rick tore open the envelope and began to read. As his eyes ran down the page, his face darkened.

"Malnutrition!" he exploded. "You've got to be kidding!" He handed me the single sheet of paper. At the end of all the neatly typed sentences describing the examinations performed and the symptoms discovered the bottom line was short and simple: "Conclusions: Malnutrition."

"Maybe when the reports come back on the other calves, you'll see some kind of pattern," I ventured as I began to clear away the lunch dishes.

"Malnutrition!" Rick repeated, ignoring my attempt to be optimistic. "The poor calf wouldn't eat for two weeks before it died. I told the vets that during the autopsy. No wonder there were starvation lesions like gelatinous bone marrow and serious atrophy of the body fat—it hadn't eaten for two weeks. What I wanted to know is *why*."

As the other reports came back, just as ambiguous, that haunting question remained. Several of the animals had ulcers, and all showed a virtual loss of body fat, but no diagnostic pattern emerged. Somewhat disheartened by the lack of clinical evidence to confirm and explain what he was seeing in the calves, Rick decided to try another possible source of help. He telephoned the dairy department at Michigan State, explained the situation with the feed, and offered to give the necessary calves to the university if they would look into the problem. Surely the professors and students there could do the research that would unlock the mystery.

To his consternation, the university rebuffed Rick's proposal to repeat the calf experiment under controlled conditions at its dairy research facility. The dairy department representative with whom Rick talked said that they lacked the facilities for such a feed trial. During the conversation, he also mentioned that they had heard nothing from other farmers or veterinarians concerning any ill effects the Farm Bureau feed was having on animals. Rick concluded that the university did not feel it was appropriate to become involved in what it saw as a squabble between a farmer and his feed supplier.

After the telephone call he fell silent. Morosely, he wandered around the house for an hour before he had the energy to try another avenue of exploration. Picking up the phone again, Rick called the East Lansing office of Dr. Grover, the Department of Agriculture veterinarian who had examined our cows for infectious diseases. Although Dr. Grover said that he himself did not have the capability to run a laboratory-controlled feed trial, he agreed to contact a Dr. Gatzmeyer at the agriculture department's Geagley Laboratory about running such a bio-assay. Within a few days Dr. Gatzmeyer had begun a feed trial giving the suspect pellets to six laboratory mice for two weeks.

A week into the experiment, Rick called the laboratory to find out how the mice were faring. When Gatzmeyer told him that the mice appeared and were acting normal, Rick was dejected. Perhaps the #402 was not the culprit after all. But a second call, after ten days of the test, gave Rick his first solid bit of evidence that there was indeed something wrong with the feed: "All of the mice in the experiment have died," Dr. Gatzmeyer reported drily. "They went from thirty grams of body weight to twenty grams of body weight in ten days, but they ate the feed heartily. Some of them even died with feed in their mouths."

Rick was shocked that the supposedly nutritious feed would be so uniformly lethal. "Could you run the experiment again just to be sure of the results? I have to be positive the feed is at fault before I contact the feed company."

Between Christmas and New Year's Day, when the mouse trials had been completed, Rick called Don Armstrong, the executive vice president of Farm Bureau Services in Lansing, to fill him in on the problems with the feed. He described the beginning of the trouble with the dairy herd and the drop in milk production; and then told of Mark's experiment with the weaned calves, leading to the inconclusive studies by the diagnostic lab at Michigan State.

"I was shocked that the calves would rather starve than to eat the pellets," he explained. "So at my urging Dr. Grover contacted Dr. Gatzmeyer at the agriculture department, who agreed to run some tests in the lab using mice under controlled conditions. In order to be certain he ran the tests twice, and he just called with the results. The mice he fed the #402 pellets all died within ten days of the start of the experiment."

Armstrong gave a surprised whistle, but regained his composure quickly. "I'm not qualified to say how adequate those pellets are as rodent feed," he said cautiously. "But it sounds like there may be something there that cattle don't like to eat. Can you send me those test results, Rick? I should have them for my records."

"Sure. I'll mail them to you."

"We take such care in formulating, processing, and handling at the feed plant," Armstrong continued. "I can't believe those pellets could be causing any trouble. I'm going to ask Jim McKean, our staff vet, to repeat the mouse trials to see if he can find out what's going on. Maybe there was something about the way you stored or handled the feed that caused some spoilage. I'll get back to you in a few days or so."

Rick was not surprised at the feed company executive's careful and measured reply. He had known him for years as a responsible person, who was attuned to both the needs of the farmers' cooperative and of the individual farmers it serviced. His decision to seek further evidence of the toxicity of the pellets was reasonable and under other circumstances might even have seemed reassuring. But if he was somewhat impatient at being put off, Rick had no doubt that the necessary evidence **53** would be forthcoming; and he returned to his daily rounds to await a call from Armstrong to set up a meeting about the problem.

6

THE YEAR ENDED with the problems unabated. The loss of $80,000 since the production drop in September weighed heavily on us and we did not look forward to telling the employees that there would be no year-end bonus for 1973. But the consequences of this for the future were even more serious: our milk base for the coming year had been lowered; and although Rick and his father planned an appeal, they had little hope of winning back the old quota. The pervading anxiety made the holiday season less festive than usual.

In a typical winter, the snow cover in the fields reduces the daily round of chores. But this year, Rick was busier than usual. Many of our fresh cows, those which were ready to calve, were not displaying the normal signs that let the dairy farmer know the birth of a calf is near. There was no room in the birth canal of these cows for the calves to present in the normal fashion, front legs and hooves bracketing the nose, as though in a diving position. Twenty-five of the fifty cows ready to calve in January attempted to deliver a calf with its forelegs tucked back; and the taut tissue and ligaments in the already vise-tight birth canal left almost no room for the unborn calf to be manipulated, so that its legs could be straightened and brought forward to the point that obstetrical chains could be used to pull it free of its dam.

The amount of time spent in this process was critical; if the calf could not be delivered within five minutes, it was almost sure to die. Two-thirds of the calves with this new delivery problem, which Rick and his father had rarely seen before in the hundreds of births at which they assisted, were born dead. Dr. Jackson, who assisted at many of these nearly impossible deliveries, said that the calves appeared to have died three or four days earlier. Certain that this was no coincidence, he was nonetheless unable to recall any parallels in his experience or discover anything in the veterinary literature.

The final blow was having to cull these cows from the herd. With the birth of a calf, a normal cow's udder will swell like a ripe grape, ready to produce milk once again. The udders of the cows with calving difficulties looked more like raisins, shrunken and without milk. In January alone, we had to sell thirty cows for meat at the livestock auction because they were mysteriously unable to begin producing milk again.

It was not until almost mid-January that the Farm Bureau Services letter came, setting up a meeting between Rick and his father and representatives of the cooperative. Though unaccustomed to imagining themselves in an adversary position against their long-time friends and associates, Rick and his father assembled a considerable body of evidence to bolster their case that something was seriously wrong with the #402 pellets. Unless they could demonstrate conclusively that the feed was at fault there was no hope that FBS's insurance company would compensate them for their losses. They brought along computerized production records from the three preceding years to demonstrate that they had run the dairy as a successful and efficient up-to-date operation. Collecting the several laboratory reports, Rick wished that he had received a written report from Dr. Gatzmeyer on the mouse trials.

"A written report," I wondered aloud while polishing Rick's briefcase. "Isn't it clear that something terribly wrong is happening? Just reading the production records will make that painfully evident. What more persuasive data could you add? The mice died, after all, written data notwithstanding."

Rick was still coldly practical. "I don't expect them to offer me anything for the lost milk yet. FBS will undoubtedly want to do their own tests. After all, there's a lot of money at stake." Rick turned toward the mirror to tie his tie. Beneath the white shirt, his arms ached from struggling with an unborn calf that had been clamped tight in its dam's unyielding pelvis. He had had three such births to assist yesterday, and the pain crossed his face briefly. He was a quiet man, inclined toward being pragmatic and not easily aroused by physical pain or emotion. I often envied his reserve and had tried to emulate him, but the problem was gnawing away at me nevertheless.

Changing the subject as he straightened his collar, he went on, "Why don't you drive up to Grand Rapids for lunch with your friend there one of these days?"

"I will some time. First I've got to find a sitter who could take care of the children for at least four hours. And I'd like to lose a few more pounds first: the sight of overweight women in a restaurant always looks a little silly to me."

Rick smiled, but persisted. "Really, you ought to go out more often. Even if you do have to find a sitter. You've got to have some time to call your own."

I could see that he felt vaguely guilty about how things were going. Lately I had been wrapped up in fixing meals, taking messages, and watching the children. Our conversations had lost their sparkle; rarely did we seem to laugh any more about funny things that happened during the day. Maybe nothing funny was happening. Without being at the center of the gloom I seemed to have absorbed it.

The meeting was scheduled for the Battle Creek Farm Bureau office, and when Rick and his father arrived there, they were met by Tony Grusczynski, the affable manager of the Battle Creek Farm Bureau store, and Don Armstrong, the chief executive officer of Farm Bureau Services in Lansing. Over coffee from the office percolator, Ted began to outline the complaint that had brought them there. As he described the story, the original friendly mood gave way to a grim and businesslike seriousness. When Rick described the diagnostic tests at Michigan State, Don Armstrong interrupted.

"Would you mind signing a release so that we can look at those lab reports?" he asked.

Rick hesitated: this was not the way he liked to do business. He was uncomfortable at the thought of a legal document giving the Farm Bureau free access to the results of work he had had done. Would he be opening the way to misinterpretations that might jeopardize any chance for a settlement?

"I'll need both of your signatures," Armstrong added, passing a document across the table. In the hope that free and open exchange of information would eventually help solve the problem, Rick consented to the release and signed his name.

When the two dairymen had finished their account, Armstrong disclosed that Farm Bureau Services had also arranged for some tests of the #402 pellets. Agway of Fabius, New York, would run feed trials on four groups of four calves each with the pellets; and Wisconsin Alumni Research Foundation, WARF, would do some further tests of the feed. If anything turned up, Rick would be notified, probably within a month or so.

"You can be sure that we'll get to the bottom of this," Don Armstrong added, giving Rick and Ted more assurance of FBS's concern.

Armstrong's willingness to solicit the tests on the feed restored Rick's confidence. In the casual clatter of a nearby cafeteria, where the four of them adjourned for lunch, the tension dissipated and the men exchanged reminiscences from the days when Armstrong had managed the Battle Creek Farm Bureau Services store.

The discussion turned to liability insurance; and Rick asked Don his opinion of the current situation.

"I'll tell you honestly, we decided to get some more insurance last year. There was a case in Flint where a gasoline tanker overturned on an interstate highway overpass and caught fire. Nobody was injured too badly, but the overpass was burned to the extent that they had to tear it down and replace it. Do you have any idea how much an overpass costs?"

Rick shook his head.

"The company that owned the tanker had to pay for the whole job—from demolition to painting the stripes on the new road. The whole business ran several million dollars." He lowered his voice. "We had a million dollars in liability insurance last year—total."

Rick was surprised. With sales of $150 million a year, he had expected that FBS would carry $10 or $20 million in insurance. "What do you have now?" he asked.

"Five million," Armstrong replied.

Rick did not respond to what he considered a lower figure

than prudent. Instead, he remarked on the recent astronomical settlements that some juries were handing out in personal injury claims. "One accident could easily wipe out a small business man," he said grimly.

Though Rick and his father were pleased, overall, with the meeting, the decision of the feed company to do further testing meant more waiting. While they awaited the results of those tests, Rick had a telephone conversation with Jim McKean, the Farm Bureau Services staff veterinarian. Rick had learned that Dr. Gatzmeyer had repeated the mouse feeding trial for McKean at the FBS veterinarian's request, and that again all of the mice had died. Convinced that these unassailable test results would sway McKean's confidence that there was nothing wrong with the #402 pellets, Rick began, "I hear that the mice who were fed the #402 pellets in your test died. Don't you think that proves something's wrong with the feed?"

But McKean thought he had a new explanation for the test results. "This is cattle feed, not mouse food," he said. "Apparently it lacks an amino acid that mice need in order to function properly."

Rick was incredulous. "Oh come on, McKean," he retorted. "You know as well as I do that mice can live on newspapers. They should have thrived on that high-priced cattle feed."

But McKean was adamant; and Rick was equally unwilling to back down from his certainty that something in the feed was toxic. He had seen too many mice living on virtually nothing to believe that they could starve while eating the pellets.

A letter from Federal Milk Market Administrator McLeary arrived on January 17 and confirmed our worst suspicions. The unexplained drop in production, despite the mounting evidence that it resulted from feed that was tainted through no fault of our own, did not qualify as the sort of "extraordinary circumstance" which would allow us to retain our old base. No matter now if we somehow managed to attain last year's production levels: we would have to sell much of it as surplus at greatly reduced rates.

"What would be an extraordinary enough circumstance?" I asked bitterly.

"Well, there are three conditions," Rick said. "If we would

lose our barn due to a fire or windstorm; if we'd lose more than 50% of the herd to brucellosis or tuberculosis; or if we'd be quarantined for pesticide or herbicide residue."

"I don't see the difference—"

"Those are the regulations, I guess," Rick shrugged.

"And I suppose the bureaucrats in the Department of Agriculture can't ever make exceptions. What ever happened to the idea of government serving people instead of the other way around?"

In a few days my attention was wrenched from the health problems the cows were having to my own physical condition. I had finished washing my hair one afternoon and had begun drying it when suddenly I began to feel excruciating chest pains. Since I also felt light-headed, I put my head down for a few minutes, then called Rick at the barn office to ask if he could come home quickly.

59

I lay down on the couch and waited an interminable five minutes before he arrived. "Thirty-year-old women do not have heart attacks," he announced as he walked in the door, trying to sound cheerful. He sat down on the couch and took my pulse. It was rapid and steady. He walked over to the bookshelf to refer to one of the medical textbooks he had purchased on a recent trip to the bookstores in East Lansing. After reading through the "heart attack" section twice, he seemed confident that those symptoms were not present; and he turned to the section on heat exhaustion. "Maybe you got too warm under that hair dryer," he suggested. "Let me get you some of that fruit and sugar syrup we had on our cake for dessert last night. Maybe that will perk you up a little."

"But my diet!" I argued.

"That can wait," he replied firmly. "Just relax while I make the lunch. We'll see if you feel better in 30 minutes."

My pulse had slowed down and the pain had eased enough for Rick to return to his work after lunch. But a couple hours later, the pains returned.

I called the barn once more. "Rick, it's happening again. I called your mother. She's going to watch the children while I go to the doctor to have this checked. I'm worried."

"Do you feel well enough to drive?"

"Yes, it isn't too bad right now. I can make it to Battle Creek."

"You're sure?"

"Yes."

I put the children into the car and began the five-mile drive to Rick's parents' place. The children, usually boisterous in the car, seemed to sense the gravity of the situation; and they talked only in whispers, if at all. When we got to the house, Rick's mother was on the steps to greet us. "Are you sure you're well enough to drive?" she asked.

"Yes, I can get there on my own."

It would have been a beautiful day for a drive if my chest hadn't hurt so. I was baffled by the pain. For months I had been putting myself through an exercise program with the doctor's blessing. If anything, I thought I was in better physical shape than at any time since Lisa had been born. I could run in place for at least ten minutes, and I had lost seventeen pounds.

The thirteen-mile drive to the doctor's office in Battle Creek seemed endless. The pain was getting worse. Fear began to creep up on me. I began to promise myself that I would get to a certain landmark soon; passing one, I mentally checked it off and began thinking of the next one. Inside the city limits my hands began to go numb. "I can't faint now!" I thought, looking at the steady stream of traffic all around. "Where can I go?" By now, my hands were almost completely numb, and black spots were creeping into my peripheral vision. In near panic, I turned into the first side street I saw and headed toward the hospital, which was six blocks closer than the doctor's office. My hands and feet were completely numb by the time I stopped the car and began to stumble to the emergency entrance. An orderly grabbed me and helped me to the emergency desk.

"What's wrong?" he asked gently.

"Everything is going black. If I don't lie down, I'll faint. I was going for an electrocardiogram because my chest has been hurting all afternoon. Then everything began to go black."

"You'll be all right. We'll get you to a bed and do the EKG here. The doctor can read it at his office after we get it finished." The orderly ushered me to a bed in the emergency room and stayed until a doctor appeared.

The blackness did not seem so determined to take over my field of vision, but the chest pains had not stopped, and I could not help wondering if this was where I was supposed to die—in an emergency room, with strangers all around. As if reading my mind, a bass voice sounded from the other side of the curtain, "You're too young to die!" A young doctor with curly hair followed the voice around the curtain to the side of the bed. The doctor asked me where I hurt. Furrowing his brow, he listened to my pulse and then my heart, and ordered someone to take an electrocardiogram.

"You're terribly frightened, aren't you?" he asked quietly.

"I don't know what's going on. Am I having a heart attack?"

"I don't think you came here today to die on us, if that's what you mean," the doctor smiled and patted my hand. "Are you feeling any better now?"

61

"There isn't so much black in my field of vision, but my chest still hurts."

"We're going to run a few tests on you now—an EKG and some X-rays. Had any falls or accidents recently?"

"No."

"Any history of heart problems—murmurs or rheumatic fever?"

"No."

While the nurse taped the sensing devices to my skin, I tried to relax, but it seemed impossible. Something inside of me wanted to fight back, to survive. I thought about Rick and the children, and about this lonesome hospital room. I thought about yesterday, playing a game of tag with the children on the frozen yard. Would I ever be able to do that again? Or had I been betrayed by my own body?

Tests completed, an orderly wheeled me to the hallway outside the X-ray room. "There'll be a wait here," he explained. "The technician has stepped out for a while." I tried to relax, to remember a breathing exercise I had once seen on television, but it was not working. Where was the technician? Didn't it matter to anyone that I was in the grip of terrifying pains?

After what seemed to be a half-hour wait, the technician finally showed up and, with a cheery greeting, rolled the bed into the X-ray room. I was seething. Why had this woman taken so long in getting here? Why was she so happy? Afraid of stressing myself while my chest still hurt, I said nothing. The X-ray turned out to be a routine chest X-ray. Well over an hour had passed, and I was still alive.

Back in the emergency room there seemed to be an air of casualness. No one was in a hurry. The doctor was smiling: "You're in great shape. Your electrocardiogram is better than mine. When you came in, we weren't certain—but now we think you were suffering the effects of hyperventilation. You were frightened by something—probably the chest pains—and you were getting too much oxygen. That's what caused the black spots and the numbness in your hands. The chest pains are more of a mystery—but you aren't having a heart attack. We'll send you along to your own doctor for a diagnosis in his office, but you'll have to have someone else drive you there. These things have a way of recurring."

Since Rick was milking that day, I called his sister to drive me to the doctor's office. The wait there seemed endless. I tried to occupy my mind by concentrating on old sports magazines, but the chest pain would not allow itself to be ignored. Finally my time came. The doctor looked at the electrocardiogram, asked a few questions, and diagnosed the episode as a "case of nerves." I left with a prescription for a vial of yellow pills, which I was supposed to take whenever I felt nervous, along with an aspirin to ease the chest pains. The doctor had no idea how long the problem would last, but doubted that it would worsen.

Still convinced that the toxicity of the feed pellets had probably happened before, Rick had continued reading through veterinary books, searching for any clue that might lead to the answer. He had even borrowed a toxicology text from Dr. Jackson, who apologized that the book was a few decades old. "With new chemicals and poisons coming onto the market every day, it's virtually impossible to keep up with this field," the doctor said. "You're welcome to this; I wish I had more to offer."

As a matter of fact, the doctor did have more to offer; and he called Rick often to add new bits of information to what was available in the books. The mysterious ailment that had befallen our cattle so absorbed Dr. Jackson that he was putting in time on it "after hours," despite Rick's insistence that he bill us for whatever time he was spending on the problem. Late one night he called with a hopeful bit of information. Reading a veterinary journal he had come across the name of another researcher who might be able to help us by analyzing the feed. Rick was cautious: there had been too many dead ends already to chase another false alarm. "Who is he?" he inquired.

"I just read a journal article by a Dr. Pier, of the National Animal Disease Laboratory—the NADL—in Ames, Iowa. This article is about his work with mold toxins—mycotoxicosis—in feed. I thought I might give him a call—with your permission, of course—and see if he'd be interested in working on your feed problem. From this article it seems as if there's a chance that a mold toxin might be your problem."

"I'd wondered about that myself," Rick said, "but I didn't know where to look for someone really qualified to analyze the feed for mold. You remember that Don Hillman's test on the high-moisture corn found nothing but some yeast growth."

"Well, I don't know what kind of setup they have at the NADL," Dr. Jackson said, "but this might be worth a try."

"Certainly," Rick said. "Let me know if he's willing to look at the problem."

After hanging up the phone, Rick went to the bookshelf to read more about mold toxin symptoms. Considering how familiar a substance mold is, Rick was amazed at how little was known about it. Of the hundred or more mold toxins that existed, only a few can be positively identified. Consequently, a researcher might be able to say that a mold problem could exist in a given case, but yet not be able to identify the culprit further. Some of the symptoms which had shown up in our cattle did accord with mycotoxicosis: abnormal hoof growth, severely diminished milk production, pregnancy complications, and returning to heat. Maybe we were getting closer to the answer.

The phone call from Dr. Jackson to Dr. Pier convinced the expert that a mold problem was likely enough to warrant testing the feed. When the samples arrived in Iowa, Rick called Dr.

Pier, introduced himself, and filled him in on the details of the problem and the course of the investigations to date. Dr. Pier said that he was going to run the mouse feeding trials again.

Within two weeks the report came back. The mice had all died. "They certainly showed a refusal factor," Dr. Pier said.

"Could you discuss this 'refusal factor' further, Dr. Pier?" Rick asked. "No one reported that in any of the mouse trials run by the Michigan Department of Agriculture."

"Well, they seemed to refuse to eat the feed," Dr. Pier explained. "In many cases, the mice would rather starve than eat it. As a consequence, their body weight dropped by about one-third. To all appearances, the mice starved. That's a very dramatic example of a 'refusal factor.'"

Rick recalled the calf experiment. "The Michigan State diagnostic lab said that the calves we took there for post-mortem examination also showed signs of severe loss of adipose tissue. One animal in particular they said had no fatty tissue no matter where they looked. In sum, they concluded that the animals died of malnutrition—which was a pretty uncomfortable finding—and one that makes little sense, because the calves had the pellets for only ten days before we had pity on them and began to give them corn silage with the pellets sprinkled on top so that they would eat something. They just weren't eating the pellets. When we gave them the silage, they still didn't eat normally—one of them never ate anything after having the pellets. It just acted like your mice, refusing even the corn silage. I think that was one of the first ones we took to MSU. Several of the calves would only come around if we gave them fresh whole milk. They drank that as if their lives depended on it."

"I can't see any evidence of a mold problem in these pellets, but I did notice something odd about them," Dr. Pier said slowly. "Have you noticed that some of them appear to be frosted?"

Rick had often rolled the pellets in his hands as he had walked by the mound on the mow floor, idly hoping for some insight into the problem. He recalled the frosty look some of them had, but had not considered it important.

"We decided to give some of the mice only the frosted-looking pellets," Dr. Pier reported. "The mice that got those died faster than the others. And they showed the "refusal factor" more than the rest. It would take some analysis, of course, but that frosting may have something to do with the problem."

"Let me check with the feed plant about the cause of the frosting. Maybe they have an explanation for it."

But no one at the feed plant seemed to know why the pellets appeared frosted, so Rick somewhat hesitantly called Jim McKean in Lansing.

"Jim, this is Rick Halbert. I'm having some tests run on the #402 pellets, and Dr. Pier at the NADL in Iowa has discovered something I'd like to pursue with you if I could."

"Of course. What would you like to know?"

"Dr. Pier has noticed that some of those pellets are different in appearance from the others. Most of them are greenish, but some are frosty-looking. I was wondering if you could tell me what in the formula could cause that frosty appearance?"

McKean checked his records and called Rick back at once. "We've had a caking problem with the formula," he explained. "So we had to add calcium carbonate to keep it from caking. What you're seeing is simply calcium carbonate."

Rick called Dr. Pier back. The toxicologist was not convinced by McKean's explanation. "Would that explain why the mice refuse the food?" he asked. Dr. Pier went on to explain that the NADL had decided to try giving solvent extractions of the #402 feed to some mice through stomach tubes, hoping that this would isolate some toxic factor. But the stomach-tubing experiment proved as inconclusive as the rest. The mice were less harmed by the extractions of the feed than those who were given the feed itself.

At the end of January Dr. Pier called to tell Rick that his experiments were over. "You might have a problem with a mold toxin we can't identify," he admitted, "but I've exhausted my capabilities on it. I did show it to one of my colleagues in animal toxicology, and he seemed quite interested in your problem. His name is Al Furr, and he will probably be running some tests of his own."

Rick thanked Dr. Pier for his efforts. His apprehension at having to make yet one more contact to persuade yet one more research group to attack the mystery dissolved quickly in his first phone call with Dr. Furr. "I'm not sure our group can find the cause of the problem," the second toxicologist conceded, "but we're certainly interested in this situation. Can you get some more of the feed to us so we can run some of the standard screenings for pesticides?"

"Sure," Rick said.

"Could you also have your vet take some tissue and blood samples that we could run for pesticides?"

Rick knew that there were small quantities of many pesticides in every food item we eat. However, a few days later he was shocked to hear from Dr. Furr that the #402 pellets tested negative for the known pesticides, but that there was 6% urea in the pellets. This finding was at variance with tests they had already run in Michigan on the samples. Jim McKean was equally incredulous. Immediately, Rick and the Farm Bureau Services both solicited further tests for urea. The tests were still negative.

Disappointed that another lead had turned out to be a red herring, Rick dialed Dr. Furr's number in Ames. The toxicologist apologized for the confusion caused by his laboratory's erroneous findings. "By the way," he added, "we did discover something that may be significant, though we can't interpret the result."

"What is it?" Rick asked.

"We've been running some tests on your feed with a gas liquid chromatograph," Dr. Furr reported. "Are you familiar with that equipment?"

Rick said that he was. He had seen chemists use them several times while working on a project at Dow Chemical. The gas liquid chromatograph, or GLC, is a device that indicates the presence of organic molecules in a sample by passing a gas such as nitrogen through a liquid extraction of the sample and recording the results on a printout. The chemist begins by grinding up the material to be tested—often using an ordinary kitchen blender—and mixing it with an ether-like solvent that will extract the unknown compound. This solvent is then filtered to remove any impurities that might interfere with the GLC's operation. The "cleaned up" sample is injected with a microsyringe into the GLC, where the gas is run through it and into a long coiled tube. As the gas leaves the tube, a needle records the presence of the unknown agent in the extract. Lighter molecules show up first on the printout; the heavier molecules later. But if the same settings are used on the machine, the time and order of the results will always be the same—as distinctive as fingerprints.

"Well, when we left the chromatograph on for eight hours, after all the known peaks for pesticides and polychlorinated biphenyls would have shown up, we began to get a series of peaks on the printout that look like the Rocky Mountains. The pattern is something I haven't seen before, and I haven't any idea what it is. I can't say that these peaks are the mystery ingredient that caused your problem, but I thought you'd like to know we did find something."

"Are you sure you've never seen this pattern before?" Rick asked excitedly. He was not sure why the NADL lab had left their GLC running so long—but fortune, for once, seemed to favor him.

"Yes, I'm sure. We've run everything from peanuts to grass through here, but none of it has ever shown these peaks. Now you've got to remember that this pattern might not mean anything at all. On the other hand, many of the peaks are repeated in the tissue samples we got from Dr. Jackson. Whatever it is, the animal and the feed had something in common."

"Can't you run the material on a mass spectrometer?" Rick asked. "At least you could find out the atomic composition of the peaks." A mass spectrometer is a very expensive device for sorting out and identifying the atoms in a sample of material.

"That would be a logical next step," the doctor admitted, "but we don't have a mass spec here at the lab. The closest one is at Iowa State, but we'd have to find somebody to clean up our sample and then wait our turn on the list. I've considered trying to get on the list, but a lot hinges on first finding someone to clean up the sample."

Rick understood the problem of cleaning up the sample. It was a necessary process which removed compounds that might interfere with the analysis of the feed. One could not throw a handful of something into the sensitive instrument. It was so specialized a task that there were different clean-up extractions to be done for each class of chemicals. But he was surprised that so large a laboratory did not have its own mass spectrometer. "I'd really appreciate it if you could find a way to get the sample prepared and checked out at Iowa State," Rick pleaded.

"I can understand your anxiety," Dr. Furr said sympathetically. "After all this time, I can imagine how desperate you must be to identify this stuff. But we're having some serious funding problems here, and I may not be able to get the money to pay someone to prep the sample. But I'll do my best."

The funding problems were a recurring theme in conversations with Dr. Furr. Begging for money seemed to be an inevitable accompaniment of the job at NADL. On a smaller scale, we were beginning to realize how research could cost money. Since Rick had begun his investigations, our monthly telephone bill had soared into the hundreds of dollars. Yet he allowed himself to hope that a return on the investment was just around the corner.

7

ONE OF THE enduring struggles of the dairy business is sanitation. Rick and his father were justly proud of the efforts they spent maintaining the highest standards of cleanliness on the farm. With a herd of four hundred cattle, the sheer physical task of dealing with manure is prodigious; thirty tons each day are produced, and a significant part of the men's regular routine was devoted to pumping out holding tanks, spreading manure on the fields, replacing the sawdust used as bedding in the freestalls, and similarly unappealing but absolutely essential tasks.

On February 12—we would remember the day because of Stephanie's excitement at breakfast over a special Lincoln's Birthday project her teacher had promised the class—Rick and Ted decided that the crisp but sunny weather offered a good opportunity to drive to Battle Creek for some truckloads of fresh sawdust. As they discussed the work assignments for the day, it occurred to them that the empty liquid manure tank, hitched to one of the big tractors in the driveway nearby, probably ought to be returned across the fields to the barn, so that the waste tank under the holding area could be pumped out.

"Karl should rebuild some stalls at the barn," Rick's father suggested. "Why don't we have him drive the tractor and tank back there—it'll save someone else a trip later."

"I don't envy him the cold mile and a half ride, but he never seems to mind."

It was true. The quiet bachelor was in many ways an ideal farm worker. Clever, creative, responsible, he could be relied upon to perform a wide range of tasks, but he didn't complain about annoying jobs which a less dedicated worker might have tried to postpone, perhaps indefinitely. After Karl was given his work assignment he climbed onto the seven-ton John Deere tractor and pulled his collar up around his neck. Rick drove off for Battle Creek in the truck.

An hour later Rick returned with the first load of sawdust to the freestall barns where an obviously agitated Gordon was waiting for him.

"Some fool has been leaving the tractors with their engines running and the transmission in neutral instead of park," Gordon began in exasperation. Rick blushed slightly. Maintaining the tractors was Gordon's particular responsibility, and the habit he was now complaining about was an unsafe practice, but Rick had to confess that he was guilty of it once in a while himself.

"We'll have to talk to the other men about that." Rick was about to explain that it was only the loader tractor that he ever left in neutral, figuring that with the bucket down in the bunker silo it couldn't move very far even in the unlikely event that it would jump into gear. But Gordon was continuing excitedly.

"Jim and I just had to catch the 4520 a couple minutes ago. It had gotten away and it was tearing through fences back by the silo. I don't think it did any damage to the tractor, and we're lucky it didn't hit one of the buildings. But we have got three fences to fix—all because somebody was careless."

"Any idea who?" Rick asked.

"Beats me," Gordon snapped. "Come on, take a look. Jim chased down the tractor and stopped it over there." He gestured toward a low spot between a fold of hills behind the barn. At the scene, two stock fences lay around the tractor in a tangled disarray; their posts had been zipped neatly out of the frozen ground. The empty manure tank was still hooked to the nearby tractor. Something suddenly occurred to Rick.

"Seen Karl this morning?" he asked.

"No, why?"

"I sent him over here with that tractor and manure tank after breakfast."

"Well, leaving it running doesn't sound like the sort of thing Karl would do," Gordon muttered. "Anyway, if you find him could you ask him to come over here to fix those fence posts?"

The loose tractor bothered Rick. After Gordon had returned to feeding the cows, Rick began to retrace the tracks of the errant tractor. It seemed implausible that Karl would leave the tractor in neutral while off doing something else; Karl was the most fastidious employee they had. He was, if anything, the antithesis of carelessness. As he walked along the wide chevron patterns the tractor had left in the snow, Rick felt a growing sense of fear.

The tracks wandered about two hundred feet from the well-marked lane that crossed the fields between his father's original farm and the milking setup. Rick noticed that the tractor had come up over a hill at a strange angle, and there was no sign of tracks running along the lane where Karl would have brought the tractor through on his trip to the barn. His apprehension increasing, Rick began to jog beside the tracks which meandered aimlessly wherever the random twists of the steering wheel had led the tractor as it was jostled by the bumps in the field. A cold, sharp wind burned his lungs, and the frosty air seemed to be trying to freeze his nostrils shut. At the top of a hillock about three hundred yards from the barn, his vague fear gave way to the grim realization of the truth.

The evidence of the tragedy was before him. Karl lay in the tracks made by the heavy tank, face up in the snow, arms out to each side, almost as if he had decided to roll off the tractor in the child's game of "snow angels." Rick took a sharp breath and yelled to him: "Karl!" His voice was lost in the wind. He called again, but the fallen man made no sign of hearing.

Turning from the motionless figure, Rick ran back over the hills to the milkhouse. Hands shaking, he dialed for an ambulance. The dispatcher at the emergency center seemed to be terribly slow, asking for every piece of information twice, as if she had come to the area from another planet. "Please hurry!" he heard himself plead. He replaced the receiver while he searched out the number of the mill where his father had gone to pick up another load of sawdust.

"There's been an accident with the tractor and the manure tank. Karl is hurt, and I think that he's probably dead."

Ted Halbert was aghast. In his years as a dairyman he had stressed safety to his hired men and had insisted that everyone respect the dangers of working with large animals and heavy equipment. The care had paid off; no injury more serious than a broken thumb had ever interfered with the operation. "Have you called the Rescue Squad?" he asked.

"Yes, but they're not here yet."

"Anyone else?"

"No. I just ran back and called the ambulance."

"I'll stop at Karl's parents' house and tell them on my way. Find Nile and tell him what you know. Have Gordon get a tractor warmed up. The snow is pretty deep, and an ambulance might have trouble getting back down the lane. Don't forget to put the chain on the back of the tractor. You'd better call home, too. The ambulance driver might not have gotten the directions right."

Grief-stricken, Rick's mother had called me with what she knew of the macabre events of the morning. Too stunned for tears, I left the children playing and walked out in the cold to the half-finished garage. Building it was the last of the many jobs Karl had worked on in our old house. Standing on the threshold of the doorway to the garage, I began to cry. This was the only legacy Karl would leave besides memories—the still-unfinished wood panels, the clever details no one else had thought to add. I could clearly picture him as he had been, striding up the hill between the calf barn and the shed, toolbox in hand, trousers bloused in his boots army-style, and the familiar billed cap on his head.

At first we had never exchanged more than a greeting, but when he began to help at the house, he finally began to talk. He could remember the reasons for water tanks in the attics of old houses; he knew how to repair some missing trim along the roof in the back of the house; he recalled who the local builders had been years ago. The children had followed him around as he worked in the garage, and he would pretend to let them help measure a board or hold the nails while he put something up. Stephanie and Kristen had drawn a preschooler's interpretation of the work they had done, making sure to get every detail in the picture. When they gave Karl the picture, I saw him fold it carefully and put it in his toolbox. Though few words had been spoken, it seemed to be as serious an occasion as the exchange of a great treasure. The quiet bachelor had taken the picture home and the children stored the memory of the tall, thin man who taught them to use a hammer and got their sleds down from the garage attic when the first big snowflakes of the season began to fall.

I had hurt his feelings once—and I winced at the memory. The problem now seemed so trivial. To avoid the work of hand-digging a vegetable garden every year, we had hit on the idea of reserving as large a section of the cornfield nearest the house as we needed. The tractor would plow and harrow the cornfield for spring planting; and then we would put in our own garden in land already prepared. Last spring, after planting the garden, I had gone shopping one afternoon. Rick had told Karl to spray the cornfield with herbicide, never thinking of the still barely distinguishable vegetable plot which it **73** included—for which the weed killer would be fatal. As I pulled into the driveway, I saw the old John Deere 50 slowly traversing the long rolling field by the house, pulling the sprayer tank.

Knowing at once what had happened and that it was too late to remedy it, I jumped out of the car nonetheless and ran across the field, waving my arms to stop the tractor. Karl stopped the machine, backed off the throttle, and pulled off the ear protectors that spared him the worst of the tractor noise. "Hello, Mrs. Halbert. What can I do for you?"

"Where have you sprayed?" I asked, trying to sound calm while yelling at the top of my voice.

"From the fencerow in, about two rounds," he replied calmly. Then, as an afterthought, "Why?"

"You sprayed my garden!"

I saw a flash of pain in his eyes, and I instantly regretted having said anything. Karl and his aging parents—his father was in his mid-eighties—were avid gardeners themselves; and they had sold their produce at a roadside stand as long as Rick could remember. For the rest of that summer, Karl sent hand-picked berries home with Rick, often placing the boxes in the pickup when no one else was around to see. That was the kind of person he was: without calling attention to what he was doing, he left no end dangling, no debt unpaid.

It was late afternoon before Rick returned to the house. It

was the first time I had ever seen deep sorrow on his face. Wordlessly, searching for some comfort, we embraced. Finally, he broke the silence.

"What did you tell the children?"

"The truth—without too much detail."

"How did they take it?"

"I think Stephanie cried. She spent a long time up in her room when she put her school things away. Kristen was frightened and wanted to be cuddled a lot. I don't think Lisa understood, though she senses from the other two that something tragic has happened."

We sat in silence through supper, paying little attention to Stephanie's report of her day at school. The children went to bed early; and Rick and I spent much of the evening lost in our respective thoughts of Karl, saying little. For once, the day's stack of mail lay unopened. I kept coming back in my mind to the incident last spring about the spraying of the garden. I was grateful that Karl and I had been on amicable terms since then.

Rick told me later of the ominous fear that he had begun to dwell on that sad evening: it had grown out of a remark of his father as they had sat silently in the barn office that afternoon. Karl's father had requested an autopsy, since there was no outward evidence at the site of the accident as to what might have caused an experienced farmhand to fall from a tractor when he was fully aware of the dangers of the situation.

"One thing bothers me," Rick's father had said. "Karl helped me bag those #402 pellets at the bottom of the storage bin when we emptied out the feeder in October. He even climbed into the bin itself. Then he hauled them over to the pink barn. Maybe all that contact with the feed did something."

"I don't know if just handling that stuff could hurt anyone," Rick demurred, outwardly skeptical. "If so, we're all in trouble, because all of us came into contact with them."

For weeks following the tractor accident, Rick was troubled by the association his father had made between the accident and the feed. There was simply no way of knowing whether the feed could affect humans who breathed in its dust, or ate meat from the animals to which it had been fed. As Rick pondered the problem, he realized that it was beginning to influence his whole outlook. He had become withdrawn, and was very depressed—he rarely spoke to anyone.

Rick had never told anyone that he had tasted the pellets in a primitive attempt to find out what was wrong with them; now, the folly of his ignorance began to haunt him daily. Each time he showered he would methodically check the growth of his nails, looking for thickening where there had been none before. From time to time he would start at the slightest sign that anything might be amiss—pains under his rib cage, a tight feeling in the stomach, tiredness, indigestion. He had no idea of what he might have done to himself.

The autopsy report left the cause of Karl's sudden death virtually unexplained. Stoically, we tried to accept yet another awful mystery. None of us was willing to lay the blame on the pellets without definite proof, but for years afterward the question would recur. It was impossible, in any case, to dismiss the fear that the same unknown plague that had ravaged the dairy herd had now broadened the scope of its victims to include the people who tended the cows. The effect of the feed on the dairy herd and on the calves was painfully obvious; its consequences for mice under laboratory conditions could not be denied; we also had suspicions that the small barnyard animals—the rats and the cats—were poisoned by it. At NADL in Iowa, Dr. Furr had begun testing it on pigs, steers, and ducklings.

A terrifying episode with one of the farm dogs, a German shepherd which Rick's mother had raised from a pup, added to our misery and the growing, if irrational, fear that a curse had fallen on us. Rick's father had gone out one evening to check the cattle waterers, which had been freezing up on some cold nights, leaving a mooing huddle of thirsty heifers. More as a reflex than anything else, he called for Major, the big German shepherd that ran freely on the farm.

The fawn and black dog trotted out the shadows by the pump house, but shied away from his master and slunk instead along the fence. When Major passed under the bright yardlight, Ted let out a gasp. The dog seemed to be covered with blood. He called the dog to him, watching for signs of injury but saw none. Ted realized that the dog was bloody with a recent kill, not with an injury. Ted's prized pair of swans was wintering in the shelter of the barn, in an unused calf pen. The dog could have crawled beneath the rails of the pen and killed the land-locked birds: Ted had little doubt that Major was capable of such a deed, for he had seen him tear apart many a woodchuck and barn cat in a single-minded hunt.

Running now, unmindful of the slippery driveway or his stiff back, Ted grabbed a scoop shovel that had been left against the fence after unloading calf feed. Something about Major's behavior had vaguely bothered him that afternoon, but he had merely shooed him out of the barnyard and forgotten it.

When he got to the pen where he had put the swans, he was relieved to see them both still there, rising clumsily to the clamor of his flapping boots. There was no sign of entry to the pen. Ted exhaled sharply. If the dog had not killed the swans, what had he gotten? He was very bloody and much too guilty.

While puzzling over the incident, Ted decided to check the waterer in the pen of fifteen young calves in the same part of the old barn. To his surprise, the large pen looked empty. When he had nearly reached the pen, he saw a sight that made his heart freeze. In the far corner of the pen was a stack of calves looking as if they had been thrown there in a pile by a mad butcher. There was no sign of movement in the tangle of bodies and legs, just a staring eye here and there. Ted clutched the shovel, mindful of the eighty-pound dog somewhere in the shadows. Slowly, he swung open the gate to the dimly lit pen and walked in to determine how much damage had been done, deliberately standing where the dog could reach him from only one direction. Something in the ghastly pile of calves moved. He blinked his eyes, suspecting that they were playing tricks on him. A leg in the pile twitched—at least one of the calves was alive.

He walked closer to the pile, forgetting his defensive corner, and reached for the calves on top. The topmost calf was breathing, but paralyzed with fear. Ted began to reassure it, lifting it off the pile. The young animals had been stampeded into the corner by the dog, and had climbed on each other in their frenzy to escape. Now they lay like the living dead, afraid to move, their eyes huge with fright. Remembering that chickens sometimes behaved like this, and that the birds on the bottom of such a pile usually suffocated, he worked faster, expecting to see a dead calf with each one he lifted from the pile.

Near the bottom of the pile, he began to see blood on the calves. Finally, he found the dog's victim. A fine four-month-old heifer that they had treated for a wound earlier that day lay near the bottom of the tangle of terrified animals, her side ripped wide open and the tattered remains of her stomach bulging out of the gaping wound. He moved her away from the other calves, and went to telephone the veterinarian.

An hour later Dr. Jackson's assistant, Pete Van Vranken, kneeling next to the calf in the light of an electric lantern, delivered the expected verdict. "I could try to sew her back together, but the rumen was torn into shreds by those teeth, and you can see how the contents are scattered in the body cavity. It's an iffy job at best, and she'd probably die anyway from peritonitis."

Ted nodded silently. The veterinarian reached into his bag for a syringe, filled it with a potent barbiturate, and slowly injected it into the calf's jugular vein. Moments later, her misery ended.

77

The problems in the dairy cows seemed to change every few weeks. They had gone from refusing feed and severe milk loss to tearing and lameness, then to a mass return to heat when they should have been with calf. Now, the hundred dry cows were showing a high incidence of calving problems, and we were continuing to sell animals for beef when they hadn't come into milk. Since we were in business to sell milk, not meat, Rick calculated that each cow sold to the slaughterhouse represented a loss of $900 income for that year.

Still concerned that several of the cattle symptoms closely paralleled X Disease—tearing eyes, calving problems, retarded udder development, and a drastic lowering of the serum vitamin A level—Mark and Rick had added extra amounts of vitamins A, D, and E to the dry cows' diet soon after the problems had begun to show up, hoping that the vitamins would help protect the cows' livers. When there was no discernible improvement, they had decided to dump bottles of concentrated vitamins directly into the water tanks on the dry cow lot, increasing the dosage twenty times.

Blood tests which Dr. Jackson ran on these cows showed that the vitamin A level was still only in the low normal range.

But the animals did seem to be responding to the vitamin therapy. There was less hair loss, and deliveries were noticeably easier.

But the cows continued to die. Dr. Jackson ran postmortem examinations on some of them, always hoping that they might notice some clue to the cause of death. But the signs were the same—enlarged and mottled livers, inflamed kidneys, almost total absence of fat, even on the heart muscle.

The veterinarian was clearly frustrated. "You'd think the diagnostic lab at MSU would have found something—with the blood chemistry or histopathology. They've got equipment there to do tests that I just can't run." He finished washing his hands and picked up his tools. "I don't know why they didn't send out the State Police to shut down that feed plant when those mice died. You'd think the state government doesn't know—or doesn't care—what's going on. Their own vets and labs have been involved in this from the start."

78

Rick had always thought of himself as a realist, but he had to admit that he was becoming more cynical than skeptical. Matters weren't helped when two of our hired men had attended a daylong seminar on mastitis sponsored by the Cooperative Extension Service. Nile had overheard the extension specialist talking to some other people about the problems we were having. He had heard the disparaging suggestion made that we were having "other problems" with the farm when the feed situation had arisen. The remark might have been interpreted several ways, but given everything else that was happening it was hard to see it as anything but malicious and unwarranted gossip.

Expecting help from the university, Rick had told the dairy department everything. Their specialists had been unable to help and had declined to assist us with further investigations.

It could hardly have happened at a less propitious time for my state of mind. Using a time-honored strategy for attacking the doldrums which were all too typical these days, I had ignored the relentless gloom of February in Michigan, planned a special dinner menu (at Rick's suggestion we had been cutting down on our meat consumption—to help us lose weight, he said), and had put on a bright hostess dress to greet him at the door.

Furious at what the men had reported from the seminar, he brushed by me without a word and went to the telephone. After making several phone calls he located the extension specialist at a motel in Benton Harbor. Not a word of greeting to the children or to me; not a word of explanation as to the cause for his evident agitation. I could piece together a little from his side of the conversation, but the children and I ate in silence and ignorance, as he chipped away at layers of misunderstanding. Twice I put his cold meal in the oven to reheat; then took it out again, put it in the refrigerator, and shut the oven off when he continued to talk. After Rick had spent two hours talking, I wasn't sure if he would finish the conversation.

Long past our usual bedtime, he came silently into the room, weary and remote, frustrated that all his discussions were bringing him no closer to solving the problem. And now we could no longer ignore what was happening to us. The adversity was not bringing us together. Tangled in my own strange frustrations, I was spending hours trying to figure out why I was so nervous and frightened. Unable to help me much, he had become impatient with the symptoms of my discomfort. **79**

Five years ago, planning our life together, we had both dreamed. But I had shelved my dreams when we had moved to the farm—hoping someday to return to them—and now the dreams that had drawn Rick away from the suburban routine had gone sour. There was still routine for both of us, I reflected bitterly. For me it was the domestic routine of raising three young children and trying to keep a house in order, while watching Rick's routine of trying to stave off the demise of a dairy farm.

No wonder that we seldom laughed anymore. Sometimes we seemed like strangers, united only in a determination to protect the children from the invisible enemy that was pulling down our world and eluding our attempts to identify and do battle with it.

8

80 THE EXPERIMENTING continued, and evidence kept accumulating that something was amiss with the #402 pellets. But the exact nature of the problem remained elusive, just out of reach of the methods being followed by the various scientists and veterinarians. The obstacles to success in this kind of research were formidable, as we were beginning to discover.

The group at Ames, working under Dr. Furr at the National Animal Disease Laboratory, seemed for a while to be making the best progress. They were giving the feed to a group of steers and a group of pigs; and thus far two of the pigs had died, one bleeding from the ears, the other bleeding from every orifice of the body. The post-mortems showed that both of them were filled with blood from massive hemorrhages.

Rick probed further. "How much of the feed do you have left?"

"Enough for about a week, I think," Dr. Furr replied.

"I ought to ship some more to you right away, then," Rick said. If the steer experiment was turning out like the others, there must be no risk of stopping it because they ran out of feed.

"Well," Dr. Furr interjected, "we've been discussing whether we ought to drive out to Michigan to pick up some more feed ourselves. Then we could take a look at your herd, so that we could compare the symptoms with those our animals are showing. Maybe that would suggest some tests that we haven't tried."

I could see the rising enthusiasm in Rick's face. "Why couldn't you take some of our animals back to Iowa to experiment on them there?" he asked Dr. Furr.

"No doubt about it, that would be the best way," Dr. Furr agreed. "But our project is hanging by a thread now. We're trying to get Washington to allocate us enough just to keep going. I doubt that there's any chance to follow through on your suggestion in the near future."

"Any progress?" I asked Rick after he finished the phone call.

"I think so. The Ames group is talking about driving up here next week to pick up more of the feed and have a look at our cows. I'm going to get the diagnostic laboratory data and the other reports we got from the Farm Bureau for Dr. Furr to look over. And I'm going to put the worst of the cows in the box stalls for them to see. I think we've finally got some heavyweights interested!"

For the next few days Rick spent most of his time getting the relevant information together. For once the long hours and busyness seemed to exhilarate him rather than drain him. He penned up several of the cows which had the most noticeable symptoms—hoof and hide changes, hematomas on their backs and hocks, and two cows with strangely increased metabolism, as if their thyroid glands were running wild. He loaded a couple cardboard drums with the suspect feed. And he paged through his records and reports to accumulate the most important facts that would help Dr. Furr understand the situation.

It was a Friday when the group was scheduled to arrive, but since they had said something about stopping in Lansing on the way to pick up a state veterinarian, Rick doubted that he would see them before noon. He whiled away the morning in routine tasks. At lunchtime I could tell that his mind was not on the food in front of him, and he quickly decided to return to the barn. With each vehicle sound in the barn driveway, his pulse quickened, but the afternoon milking began and ended with no sign of the party from Ames.

Rick treated the sick cows and walked back to the milkhouse through the barn. The holding area was empty, and Nile was alone in the milking parlor, puttering with the maze of hoses on the storage rack.

"See any vets yet?" Rick asked, not daring to hope for an affirmative answer.

"Nope. Nobody's come around." Nile said, not looking up from his work. Rick left the parlor in dismay. If something had delayed their arrival, they would surely have called. Had he misunderstood the date Dr. Furr had suggested? Was the Iowa group planning to come on Saturday instead of Friday? He went into the barn office to put his box of veterinary supplies away; while he waited, he straightened the desk. The neat pile of laboratory reports glared up at him; all of his careful preparatory work had been done, but there seemed to be no letup in letdowns.

At nine o'clock, Rick finally gave up waiting and went home, feeling a little silly that he had probably confused the date. Tomorrow he would probably find a bunch of official-looking strangers on the milkhouse doorstep, armed with sample bags. I reported that no word of a delay had been phoned to the house, so Rick went to bed assuming that he had made a mistake.

Saturday morning Rick sprang into his truck at seven o'clock; they will surely be here today, he thought. By noon the same day-old uneasiness began to grip him. He realized something must have gone wrong. He called me several times to see if Dr. Furr had phoned—though he knew I would have passed such a message along at once. He skipped lunch to work unenthusiastically at a few chores in the barn area. The whole afternoon crept by. There was no way to find out what had happened. Rick knew from earlier calls that the government offices were closed on Saturday.

The rest of the weekend passed slowly. Again, his hopes had been dashed, and there was little he could do for the time being but wonder what had happened. Why had Dr. Furr's group decided not to come after they had been enthusiastic about continuing the experiment? Had Rick done something or said something to make them change their minds? And what hope was there for further research into the pellets if the NADL had dropped the project?

Monday morning finally came, and shortly after 9 a.m. Rick reached Dr. Furr. "What happened?" he asked with agitation in his voice.

The scientist's voice was equally strained. "I'm terribly sorry, Rick," he said. "Friday, after we had packed to come to Michigan, we got word from our director in Washington that absolutely no more funds could be spent on the project and that we had to stop any further work on it. We had to cancel the trip and the project. Period."

Stunned and angry, Rick said nothing, could say nothing.

After a moment of silence, Dr. Furr added quietly, "I wonder if Farm Bureau has anything to do with this."

The suspicion was one that had occurred to Rick during the long and agonizing weekend. The national parent organization of the local Farm Bureau Services outlet had a strong lobby in Washington. The recent Watergate revelations and the stories in the news of influence-peddling in government were enough to raise one's doubts about what might be going on behind the scenes. And Farm Bureau Services had not exactly been enthusiastic about Rick's insistence on experimenting with the #402 pellets.

"I hope not," Rick said. "Do you think it would help if I gave your project director a ring? Maybe I can convince him to reconsider."

"Well, it can't hurt to try. But I warn you, Dr. Cassidy, our lab director, was adamant when I talked to him about the cancellation. You should call the head of APHIS in Washington."

The director of the Animal and Plant Health Inspection Service (APHIS) of the US Department of Agriculture was a Dr. Mulhern. Rick had some trouble getting through to him, but finally he persuaded the secretary of the importance of his business. As briefly as he could, he outlined the events that had led to the research in Ames: "For the past several months, our dairy herd has been plagued by mysterious problems. Last September the cows simply stopped eating everything. Their production dropped drastically, finally stabilizing only when we had taken away all of the regular feeds and began to feed green chop. For weeks, the only things the cows would eat were green chop and dry hay. Their milk production stabilized on this regimen, but it never rose above the point of stabilization. When we tried to return them to the regular feed, they balked at the commercially produced pellets we had bought from the local co-op.

"Puzzled by this, we withdrew the pellets, and had them tested for all common toxins. The feed company dismissed the idea that there could have been contamination by machine lubricants or a mistake in the addition of nutrients to the formula, so we decided to try to feed the pellets to a group of calves. Within two weeks, those calves began to die. To corroborate our screening experiment, we went to the Michigan Department of Agriculture laboratory and they fed the pellets to mice in a controlled experiment. The mice died too.

"What we were trying to do in the Ames experiment was to find out the cause of the inappetence and, hopefully, the identity of the lethal agent." Dr. Mulhern had listened quietly to Rick's story. Now his tone was cool. "This is all very interesting, Mr. Halbert, but why hasn't anyone else in Michigan complained of problems with the feed? Why haven't other veterinarians seen anything unusual?"

The question did not surprise Rick. "Our only source of information concerning the acceptance of the feed on other farms has been the feed company. Their vet keeps telling me that no one else is having problems, but I know that one farmer near Grand Rapids who used the feed has been driven out of business by the production problems he had with his cows. And I've heard of at least one other farmer near Allegan who had some difficulties."

"Two other farmers who *possibly* had problems with the feed does not warrant the expenditure of USDA money."

The litany was beginning; somehow Rick must find a way to overcome it. "I'm convinced if your department would investigate you'd find dozens of farmers suffering as we are."

"I'm sorry, Mr. Halbert." Dr. Mulhern's voice was polite but firm. "I'm sure that Dr. Furr told you that we're having a funding problem here. A lot of worthy projects are facing cuts in their funds or are being shut down altogether. I simply can't see any way for us to allocate more money to the people in Ames."

Rick was fuming when he hung the phone up. "The most

you can ever get from these damned bureaucrats is a faint glimmer of hope. Maybe we've wrung enough out of him to keep someone working on it for a week."

In a desperate attempt to keep the project at Ames going, Rick also called Jim McKean. Since the episode in December when McKean had dismissed the death of the mice that had been given the pellets, Rick had avoided the Farm Bureau veterinarian. Now he put his personal feelings aside to plead for help. "I talked to Dr. Mulhern in Washington. He hasn't allocated more APHIS funds for the work in Ames. In light of what you know about our situation, I'd appreciate it if you'd call Dr. Mulhern and put in a word for keeping our project funded. I'm sure it would be in your best interest."

McKean was noncommittal, Rick told me when he hung up. "I think he'll call Washington, but he didn't promise." As a matter of fact, we never did learn whether the veterinarian had called APHIS.

After a few days, Rick called Ames back to see whether his request had changed the decision. There was a pause before Dr. Furr spoke. "APHIS stands by the original decision to let the project die," he said. "No more money can be spent on our experiments. Believe me, Rick, I'm as disappointed as you are. I'm having a list of laboratories made up, which I'll send to you—labs that have the capability to resolve the question of the peaks we found on the gas liquid chromatograph. Maybe one of those labs can continue the animal studies, too."

"Thanks, Al. I appreciate all your people have done, and I only wish we could have found the answer. Can you send a report on the final data from the feeding experiments?"

"Well, we'll send the data on the tests as far as we could take them."

Rick left silently for the barn. This looked like the end of the trail as far as government research was concerned. No last-minute rescues, no government agent on a white horse to pull off a miracle. We had lost a hundred thousand dollars since October and there was no end in sight. But there was to be no relief from the government, and we weren't optimistic about receiving any payment for the damage without a court battle. He looked at the cows. Throughout these tragic months they had been uncomplaining, passively accepting even the difficult calving this unknown contaminant had caused. Now they were showing signs of a strange roughness in their coats. Each hair of some of the animals seemed to stand out from the skin, as though charged with a tiny burst of electricity.

Silently feeding the cows, Rick wondered how long we could go on like this. During January they had culled more cows for low production than many farmers had in their entire herd. He noticed that the cow in the maternity stall was now beginning to calve; he stood to watch her.

After a powerful contraction she turned her head to look for the calf. The calf was slow in coming; Rick finally phoned his father for help with the delivery. Together the two of them worked on the calf, trying to free it from the cow's tight pelvic structure. The unborn calf was still: like half of the calves in the last two months it would be born dead. The strange musty smell of the calf and its puffy appearance led them to think it had been dead about four days when the cow went into labor. As they pulled the dead calf out of the birth canal, its already decaying forelegs were pulled from their sockets.

The cow nuzzled the calf, lowing to it softly, as if trying to arouse it. She began to lick it with her tongue, stopping to nuzzle it and low again, but became confused when the calf made no response. When the cow moved away from the calf, finally, Rick went into the maternity stall. The exhausted mother, standing in the far corner, as far away from the strangely still calf as she could be, made no protest as Rick lifted the calf from the stall. The other cows in the dry lot went about business as usual, unable to realize that anything was wrong.

A few days later Mark called Rick's attention to 922, a leopard-spotted cow that had been an excellent producer. "She hasn't eaten a thing for three days," Mark reported. "If that goes on. . . ," he stopped, the sentence unfinished but the meaning perfectly clear. If 922 didn't get up and start eating she too would turn into another of those wraiths that haunted the barns, waiting, maybe wanting, to die.

"How about trying to stomach-tube her," Rick suggested. "We could pump her full of nutrients every day, maybe build up her strength until she felt like living again."

"I'm game," Mark replied. "But it's pretty risky." Both of

them knew that if a stomach tube went in the wrong way, and did not get into the rumen, the cow might be drowned on the spot by having the fluid pumped into her lungs.

They mixed the most nutritious combination of ingredients they could assemble, then carried the full ten-gallon milk can to the sick animal. She looked up with little interest as they entered her stall. Mark put the can down on the straw while Rick warmed up the stainless steel sleeve in a pail of warm water. When it reached body temperature, he signaled for Mark to hold the cow's head while he forced the steel sleeve down her throat. With the sleeve in place, Mark took a long plastic hose from the pail of water where it had been warming and handed it to his brother, who forced it down through the sleeve into the cow's rumen.

Both were silent. "OK, let's try it," Rick said. Kneeling down, he blew into the plastic tube, while the two of them watched the cow's sides for signs that her stomach was filling with air.

"I can see it. It's in!" Mark said, and groped behind the pail for the pump they used to force fluid down the stomach tube. Attaching the pump to the tube, he began to pump the solution into the cow while Rick held her head. A quick reflexive toss of the head could have pulled the tube up out of the rumen and pump the fluid into the cow's lungs.

Twice a day, for two weeks, the brothers went into the stall with the milk can and gave her the life-sustaining treatment. After a few days she made no attempt to fight the uncomfortable procedure. A few days after that, they put some hay in the manger; and two weeks after they had noticed that she was beginning to starve, they found her standing one day, eating out of the manger. The process, slow and dangerous, had saved the cow's life.

The gloom and apathy that had settled over Rick, when the Ames experiments were canceled, dissipated in a matter of a week, and his scientific curiosity overcame his despair. A call to Dr. Gatzmeyer in Lansing succeeded in setting up an experiment with some mice which were fed nonsuspect complete feed cattle pellets. They thrived on the regimen, dispelling the idea— which Rick had never taken seriously anyway—that the mice which ate the #402 pellets died from malnutrition because the cattle formula was not adequate for the nutritional needs of a mouse.

"Do you know of any labs that could do studies on higher mammals on contract?" Rick asked the doctor.

"Well, there's a place called International Research and Development Corporation in Mattawan, not too far from where you are."

"Thanks a lot. I'm looking for somewhere to do some more feed trials."

After he called the private laboratory, he turned to me. "You wouldn't believe what it costs to run a simple feed trial on mice at a private laboratory," he said.

"I have no idea."

"For a trial identical to the one Dr. Gatzmeyer just ran—a simple mouse feeding experiment—we'd have to pay five hundred dollars. For a feeding trial run on primates, we can expect to pay upwards of five *thousand*."

"Are you going to have some done?" I asked.

"I don't think we can. We'd have to spend at least a hundred thousand dollars—and then our chances of success would be about one in five. If the poison we're looking for is a man-made chemical, it could be any of thirty thousand that flow freely in commerce. If it's a laboratory chemical, we're up against four million that have been synthesized. We just can't afford that."

"Well, what then? We can't afford to lose all the cattle."

"I don't know," Rick shook his head. "I wish we could find out whether those peaks they found on the chromatograph at Ames are related to this whole mess."

Because his curiosity was still piqued by the mysterious pattern NADL had found in the feed it ran on its gas liquid chromatograph, Rick decided to call WARF, the Wisconsin research facility which Farm Bureau Services had used, to see if he could have the GLC test on the feed repeated under the same conditions. When the results came back in March, Rick again saw the fingerprint of the mystery compound. The peaks Dr. Furr had found were no aberration. A follow-up test on a Colson detector showed that the compound in the peaks responded to electron capture. Don Hughes, the man in charge of the experiments, said that the compound contained a halogen—fluorine, chlorine, bromine, or iodine—and had a high molecular weight—above 400. Rick was convinced that the mystery compound was a man-made material.

An incident with a promising young bull borrowed from the country sire-proving association did nothing to diminish our growing impression that government agencies were selective in their responses. The bull had apparently eaten some of the pellets sprinkled on the silage for the calves in Mark's experiment, and he had begun to show the telltale signs of a twisted stomach—a D.A., or displaced abomasum.

Since the bull belonged to a neighboring farmer, Rick had called Dr. Jackson immediately. His diagnosis had not taken long.

"I'm sure it's a D.A.," he said. "But that animal is in such poor shape that I don't think I'd better operate on him. The veterinary school at Michigan State has special facilities; I'd recommend sending him up there. There's a good chance they might be able to pull him through."

Rick and Mark took the ailing bull and a thin cow that seemed typical of those which had lost their milk production by eating the feed to Lansing. Perhaps now the veterinarians there would reconsider their ambivalent policy concerning the feed problem. What did they have to lose by testing his cows? Surely the problem had become serious enough that trying to find a solution would in fact be a prudent use of tax money even if ours was the only farm affected—which Rick doubted.

Rick was somewhat amused by the change in student dress since he had graduated from MSU. The sprawling campus was abloom with levis, overalls and chore jackets—the polar opposite of the natty dress of his own classmates, whose anti-farm sentiment had once made Rick reluctant to admit his rural background. At the veterinary clinic, Rick had to wait a considerable time while a number of horse trailers pulled up to the loading dock.

"Things always this busy around here?" he asked a young laboratory assistant.

"This is actually a light day," the man replied, laughing.

"This place looks like a race track with all the horses around."

When the young man told Rick how many pleasure horses the clinic treated each week, and, by comparison, how many cattle were treated, he gave a low whistle. Every appearance suggested emphasis on pleasure horses rather than commercial livestock at this particular state-operated facility.

The young bull survived the operation which successfully straightened his stomach, but his condition continued to deteriorate. When Rick picked the bull up two weeks later, the veterinarians continued to ask him how much feed he was giving his animals. It was all too apparent that they thought the animals were not being fed enough. As Rick told them—for what seemed like the hundredth time—that the animals were given as much feed as they would eat, he seethed with frustration.

A week after the bull was brought home, it died. Dr. Jackson, who had made a final attempt to save it, decided to set up his own feed trial using two rabbits he had gotten from a local rabbitry.

As we were leaving the house a few nights later to buy ice cream cones for the children—the telephone rang. It was Dr. Jackson. Reluctantly, knowing how long Rick's telephone conversations tended to last these days, I handed him the receiver.

"Sorry to interrupt your evening," the veterinarian began, "but I knew you'd want to hear this: one of my rabbits had died. I went out to check on them before we left for dinner, and when I got there it was showing signs of nerve damage or brain damage. When I gave the other rabbit its lettuce, the one with the symptoms began to totter and shake in its cage. I fed the healthy-looking one, but when I put my hand into the other cage, the rabbit didn't seem to know I was there or to smell the lettuce. It just started hopping about in an agitated way and began to shake and totter again."

"Go on," Rick said, motioning me out to the car to calm the children, whose restlessness was growing fast.

"I watched the rabbit for a while, and its behavior didn't change a bit. Finally, it went into convulsions and died. My wife and I are going out for the evening, but I'll do a postmortem on the rabbit in the morning."

How could we ever pay the veterinarian for his dedication? It seemed clear that he was putting in many more hours on our behalf than were showing up on the bills. This rabbit experiment, for example, had been his own idea. He had picked up a couple rabbits from a friend who raised them for meat and kept them in a hutch in his garage, where he fed them with some of the suspect feed.

The strange behavior of the rabbits paralleled what Dr. Gatzmeyer had told Rick about the mice; some of them had convulsed before death. The calves, on the other hand, seemed only to lie down and never get up again.

The fatal effect of the pellets on small animals now seemed undeniable. We concluded that the barn cats had probably died from ingesting the toxin, whatever it was, when they ate mice that had been eating the pellets. No doubt the mice had been slowed down by the tainted pellets, which had made it easier for the cats to catch them. As a further experiment, Rick took some of the pellets to the home of a tenant who had problems with rats in a crawl space. Shortly after he set the feed out there, the rats disappeared.

All of these tests and experiments with small animals had the cumulative effect of pointing to the pellets as the source of the difficulties that had been plaguing our dairy for nearly six months. But solving the problem seemed to depend on discovering what it was in the #402 feed that had fatal consequences. For that Rick had been trying persistently to enlist the help of the Farm Bureau Services, and the strong impression was emerging that they were something less than eager to proceed. The experiment promised in January, which involved feeding the pellets to some calves at Agway Animal Research Center in Fabius, New York, had been postponed several times, and had finally begun only a couple of days before a second scheduled meeting with Don Armstrong, Jim McKean, and Farm Bureau risk manager Ken Jones in Battle Creek in February. The number of calves had been dropped from sixteen to four; even so, Rick was hopeful that the experiment would duplicate the results of Mark's experiment with the calves in December.

The atmosphere at this second meeting was less cordial than at the January one. Seated across the room from Rick and his father, the FBS representatives seemed self-assured. On the table before them were data from tests they had requested at WARF, to whom they had given *carte blanche*, they said. When

Rick saw what tests had been run, however, he was let down: only standard pesticide screenings had been made.

"As you can see," Don Armstrong was saying confidently, "there is nothing here to indicate that the feed is anything but wholesome and pure."

"Don't you think that the death of the mice in Dr. Gatzmeyer's experiments proves the opposite?" Rick asked.

But the FBS representatives refused to admit that there was even the slightest difficulty with the feed. The meeting ended with Rick and Ted confused. They had thought that FBS had been concentrating, as they were, on finding out what was wrong with the #402 high protein feed; instead, it seemed that they were more interested in letting us know what was right with it.

When Rick had gotten home and perused the computer printout of the test that WARF, the research facility in Wisconsin, had done on the feed to analyze for toxic pesticides and polychlorinated biphenyl (PCB) he found the test registered "Interference" in the PCB column. Immediately Rick called Jim McKean. "What does this 'interference' mean?" Rick had asked.

"Well, I suppose something fouled up the readings for PCB," McKean had replied. Beyond that Rick was unable to elicit any comment. Not having a definite explanation bothered him. Was the interference significant? Or had something irrelevant merely distorted the test findings, as the FBS people seemed to suggest?

Our suspicion that the feed company was holding something back abated a little the next week when FBS set up a meeting between Ken Jones, their risk manager, and Rick. Over the telephone indications had been that Jones wanted to gather some information on our case for the insurance companies, which were getting together to begin work on what now appeared to be the contamination of the #402 pellets. He had asked to meet Rick at the barn.

The rising expectation Rick had felt at the possibility of some progress diminished somewhat when he noticed the portable tape recorder Jones carried with him. "I hope you don't mind my bringing this along to help me take notes," he said amiably, "but getting it right the first time does save a lot of time."

Though hesitant about being put in what seemed to him like a defensive posture, Rick agreed to the use of the device—which turned out to be malfunctioning anyway.

"What is the legal name of your business?" Ken Jones began, reading from a sheet of prepared questions.

"Halbert Dairy Farm."

"Is your business incorporated?"

"No, it's a partnership between me and my father."

"How many cows did you have on test in September 1973?"

"Four hundred."

"And how many of them do you suspect ate the feed in question?"

"All of the cows that were in milk when we got it," Rick answered.

"How did you feed it to them?"

For what seemed like the thousandth time Rick repeated the story of last fall—the symptoms, the growing suspicions, the several tests. As the risk manager packed up his materials at the end of the interview, Rick asked him in passing, "Heard anything about the animals in the Agway study yet?"

Jones looked up, surprised. "Didn't you know? Three of them have died." The news caught Rick off guard. Finally, there was proof, from the FBS's own experiments, that the #402 pellets were harmful to the animals they were supposed to nourish.

When he returned to the office in the barn after Jones left, Rick dialed Jim McKean's number to find out some of the details of the deaths of these Agway calves. In particular, he was curious about whether the calves had exhibited the "refusal factor" that Dr. Pier in Ames had noticed.

"Rick Halbert here," he said when McKean answered the telephone. "Have you seen anything in those Agway calves yet?"

"No," the veterinarian responded. "They're doing all right."

"No problems?" Rick asked incredulously.

"I'm sure there's no problem." McKean replied.

"I just got word that three of the four have died," Rick said.

There was no response from the other end. After some moments of heavy silence, Rick continued. "Ken Jones was just here. He told me about the calves."

"If he wanted to tell you, I guess that's OK," McKean said slowly. "It's not my place to give out information."

In November we had ordered another FBS feed, #112, to replace the #402. In the process of trying to discover the nature and extent of the problem, Rick had had some of the #112 feed sent to the WARF laboratory for testing on the gas-liquid chromatograph. Now as Rick shuffled through the test reports on the #112, he discovered that the same series of peaks that had appeared when the #402 was tested were also in the supposedly uncontaminated #112, though greatly attenuated.

"We haven't escaped by switching feeds," Rick told me bitterly. "I can't see how the feed plant could have contaminated all these batches. The whole affair makes no sense at all: it's madness." For the first time in twenty years, Rick and his father contemplated finding another feed supplier.

"Does this mean that the cattle have gotten another dose of the toxin?" I asked hesitantly, fearing for the answer. The whole herd might now be contaminated, including the heifers that had just been moved to the barn—the heifers that had been our hope for recovery.

"If the peaks are the result of the presence of a toxin, it means that we've had that toxin in all the batches of feed since mid-September," Rick said. "I just wish I knew what these peaks are. We might be worrying about something completely harmless."

He dialed Jim McKean's telephone number, but the Farm Bureau veterinarian dismissed the idea that the peaks in the #112 readings proved that FBS had contaminated all the feed they had shipped to us for five months. "We don't even know what the peaks mean," he argued. "They might be something totally ordinary."

Against that Rick had no argument, only a hunch. But his anger was mounting. "You promised us an insurance settlement," he seethed. "Where is it? If we don't start seeing some progress on this problem soon, I'm going to call the FDA!"

The threat of bringing the Food and Drug Administration into the problem was one Rick had toyed idly with before, but everyone he had talked to about it had counseled against it. "The FDA is primarily a regulatory agency," one researcher had told him. "Don't call them expecting help. The best they might do is hinder the progress you're making. They don't research the causes of problems; they just police them."

Now McKean echoed the advice of the others. "You can go ahead and call the FDA," he said grimly. "But I think you'll be sorry."

9

THE ADVICE from respected persons not to bring the Food and Drug Administration into the investigation gave Rick pause; but after the NADL group had to give up the trail because their funding was cut, we had to find another avenue. One thing was becoming ever more certain: there would be no insurance settlement without test results from an unimpeachable source. What we needed was a laboratory with expertise, drive, and funding enough to carry the work the NADL had begun to its conclusion. And Rick's mental image of the FDA suggested that the agency had drive and curiosity in abundance, far beyond necessity according to some people.

In March another phase developed to the symptoms we were seeing in the barn. Many of the ready-to-calve cows were going down, never even living to see their young born. To lose a cow and a calf at the same time was an increasingly frequent occurrence, and finally Rick could stand the waiting and frustration of it no longer. He had formulated a plan to get the FDA involved. So that the FDA could get into the mystery of the feed with as little prejudice as possible and do some original work on the feed, he had decided not to tell them about the work at Ames and MDA. He reasoned that they had as much chance of finding the contaminant as anyone else. Perhaps they would find a totally new lead which would show that the mysterious peaks meant nothing. The excitement of beginning the pursuit again welled up in him as he dialed the number of the Detroit office of the Food and Drug Administration.

Rick had decided initially to approach the FDA with the question of the lead content of the Farm Bureau #402 pellets as compared to the lead analysis of other similar feeds and to the recommendations he had found in Blood and Henderson's *Veterinary Medicine*. The WARF heavy metals analysis run for Farm Bureau had shown the lead content to be between five and ten parts per million (ppm); according to the veterinary text that was above the level at which damage could be inflicted on animal systems.

Already last summer, before the present troubles had begun, Dr. Jackson had found lead in the blood of some of the animals he had tested. He had asked Rick where he thought they might have gotten the lead. Since we had been careful to use only paints that contained no lead on the farm, Rick could not imagine where they had come in contact with the metal. The doctor's reply to Rick's question about what level of lead was safe was a simple one: "There shouldn't be any at all." The presence of lead in the feed now suggested that Farm Bureau Services might have chosen a mineral preparation that had been improperly refined, or that they had chanced the use of a nonapproved mineral product.

Rick had no idea whom to contact at the FDA office; but after some juggling from one secretary to another, he found himself talking to a Mr. Dempster. "We've received a laboratory report that indicates five to ten ppm lead in some feed we've bought. I've told the supplier that this is unsatisfactory; and I'd like to ask some questions about the level of lead you consider your tolerance level in dairy feed."

"Why don't you give me a list of the questions you've got and I'll look up the policy concerning lead and call you back." Dempster seemed encouragingly businesslike. He took our telephone number and promised to reply as soon as possible.

"Okay. First of all, I'd like to know if the five to ten ppm lead in the feed is above your standard for lead in feed," Rick continued. "Second, what's the next step if that's unacceptable. How do you go about implementing the withdrawal of a contaminated feed from the market? Third, is there a level set for the amount of lead allowable in a mineral supplement for feed?"

"Have you experienced any problems that you might attribute to an excess of lead in your feed, Mr. Halbert?" Dempster asked.

"Our loss of animals in the past three months has been considerably above our normal mortality rate," Rick replied cautiously.

When Dempster called back, he had the answers that Rick had wanted, but with one interesting omission. "We don't have a tolerance level for lead in feed or mineral supplement," Dempster began.

Rick was taken aback. Lead is one of the easiest heavy metals to test for; and lead poisoning is one of the better publicized environmental problems of the day. It seemed odd that the Food and Drug Administration had no rules concerning the permissible amount of lead in dairy feed.

"When we are told of a possible contamination," Dempster continued, "we first send an inspector out to take samples of the material or materials in question. These are taken directly to our laboratory, where they are analyzed. When the data from the analysis are available, we decide whether to act on it, based on existing guidelines. If the material is above the acceptable level, we take action; if it falls below the acceptable level, we do not take action. In the case of contamination of feed for dairy cows, we would require that the producer of the item remove it from the market immediately and notify all purchasers of the item that it is unsafe for consumption. We would also monitor the animal products of those who had used the feed for contamination. If they fell above our guideline for similar animal products, we would see that they were withdrawn from the market also."

"That all seems reasonable," Rick said. "What should we expect in our own case?"

"One of our inspectors will call on you in the next day or two, and we'll begin our investigation at that point. We'll want your full cooperation, of course."

After the series of runarounds we had encountered, Rick was somewhat surprised—and comforted—by Dempster's certainty. At last, it seemed, someone had a clear-cut, ready-to-beimplemented program for working on the problem. Dempster's insistence on "full cooperation" from us bothered Rick somewhat. After all, he had not told the FDA representative about the history of tests already made, for he wanted the FDA to break some new ground in the case. That would not be done unless they went into the case with a minimum of information that would lead toward already-traveled dead ends. But Rick realized that even though a scientist might not find fault with this less-than-full disclosure, a bureaucrat probably would—and he was cynical enough by now to realize that he was more likely to meet the latter than the former when a government agency was involved.

To Rick's pleasant surprise, the next day a call came from an FDA inspector by the name of Clarence Bozarth, who worked out of Kalamazoo. The inspector wanted to set up a time to meet Rick at the barn that afternoon to ask a few questions and take samples for laboratory analysis. When Bozarth arrived at the milking setup, he immediately got a thick stack of sample bags from his car and went to work, asking Rick questions as he walked and filled the plastic bags and carefully labeled them.

"Have you lost any animals, Mr. Halbert?" he began, clipboard of forms in hand and pen poised.

"More than our share in the past few months," Rick answered. Bozarth wrote something on one of the forms on his clipboard. "Would you like some samples of our forage, Mr. Bozarth? I'll show you where we store it." Bozarth followed along, nodding at the long barns of cows. He seemed very attentive to detail, occasionally pausing to jot a note on the forms he held in his hand. At the concrete bunker silo, he began to gather samples of the corn silage from various places in the football field-sized storage pit.

"Is there any way I can get a sample from the center of the pile?" It was obvious that the FDA representative was intent on doing a very thorough job.

"You can walk on the pile, if that's what you're wondering about—we could get a sample that way." Rick led the taciturn inspector out to the middle of the silo behind the milking setup, and they dug a sample for the plastic bag that he held open in his hand.

"How long does this keep?" Bozarth gestured to the sea of chopped and fermenting corn plants that lay beneath them.

"We use all of it up in less than a year. That's one of the tricks of the trade—figuring out how much of the stuff the cows will eat between corn harvest and the first cutting of hay the next summer. I'm not sure how long it has enough nutrients left in it to be worth feeding; in fact, we never keep it more than nine months."

"They eat all of this in nine months?" The inspector let his official demeanor slip for a moment, and Rick could see that he was truly impressed by the amount of food the cows required.

"All of this, plus hundreds of tons of commercial feed," Rick replied. "I'll show you the bulk storage bin for the commercial feed next; it's right over here." They walked to the far side of the milkhouse, and Bozarth scooped some grain from the bottom of the bin. When they passed his car on the way to the inside of the barn, he stopped to put the samples in the trunk and get out more sample bags. The state veterinarians, Rick recalled, had not gathered half as many sample bags in their search for the source of the problem.

"This is our milkhouse. The bulk milk storage coolers are in the center, and the pipeline from the milking parlor is the stainless steel piping you can see coming in from there."

Bozarth followed Rick's hand with his eyes. "I'd like a sample from both tanks," he said coolly.

"We only use the larger tank now, the smaller is used for surplus storage—"

"If there's anything at all in it, even water, I'd like a sample."

"We keep it dry when it's empty." Rick did not want to sound as though he were pleading with the insistent inspector, but the idea of having the FDA take milk samples picked away at his thoughts. What if there were something there for the FDA to take action on? That would have been the last, heart-breaking straw—to find something in the milk would mean total ruin.

After he had gotten his milk sample from the larger tank, Rick took Bozarth into the milking parlor where he took samples of the parlor feed. "Is there anything else that you feed the cattle?" Bozarth asked.

"Salt, urea in the silage, magnesium oxide, and minerals.

We also have some pellets that we were feeding which we suspect may be involved. We've removed that feed from the barn and are storing it in another barn about a mile away. I'd like you to take a sample of it, too—if you don't mind."

"No, we'd like anything that you suspect might be implicated in your problem." Bozarth said, as they walked toward the storage room where they could get a sample of the salt, urea, mag oxide and mineral.

Rick took the inspector to the calf barn last. They entered the mow area of the barn, and the remaining mound of pellets stood before them—greenish and innocuous in the dim light. As Bozarth stooped to pour a handful of the pellets into his sample bag, Rick was momentarily mesmerized by the scene. He had almost forgotten how innocent the pellets looked. The mound still clung to its secret, but in the eerie midday gloom Rick was certain that somehow he would unlock the secret.

"There are two other men you might like to contact concerning similar problems, Mr. Bozarth." Rick gave the inspector the names of the farmers near Allegan and Coopersville whose difficulties with the feed sounded much like his.

The visit of Clarence Bozarth had offered Rick a small respite from his growing despair. Surely the FDA laboratory data would disclose some patterns: if their scientists had anything like the persistence of the inspector who had visited us the answer would come in a matter of weeks. Forgotten was the fear that there might be something tainting the milk we were producing.

After a week or so, Rick began telephoning Mr. Dempster's office in Detroit to see whether any hard information had turned up to justify his optimism. Each call seemed to eventuate in a polite brushoff, and Rick began to have the uncomfortable feeling that he was not privy to information pertinent to his own situation.

Despite the chill in his relationship with Jim McKean, and despite the fact that McKean had advised against going to the FDA, Rick had decided to mention to the FBS veterinarian that he had taken that step. McKean's response had been guardedly encouraging: "If you don't hear from the FDA, don't worry. The time you should be worrying, they'll be right there, making sure that you're worrying."

With the passing days, it became clearer that the regulatory agency had probably run into a dead end on the examination of the feed for lead. Whatever tests they had run, they had apparently failed to find the killer ingredient or even anything that piqued their curiosity. Perhaps the time had come to offer some more information to Dempster, in the hope that such additional clues would propel the the research a littler further. From his files he pulled out the data on the gas liquid chromatograph test from Ames, and dialed the Detroit office of the FDA.

"I've got something here that might help in finding the cause of our problem," he began. "Some time ago, we sent some of the feed that we think is causing the problem to the National Animal Disease Laboratory in Ames, Iowa. When the lab there ran a sample of the feed through their gas liquid chromatograph, they got a series of long, slow peaks hours after materials such as pesticides and PCB would have come out. The scientist who ran the test said it should be looked into further, but they had no more funds for testing."

But Dempster was unexcited. "I'm sorry, Mr. Halbert, we're just not a research organization. The Food and Drug Administration can't take action unless we know what the problem is. You'll have to get someone else to do the work. If you get some more information, we'll see if we can act further."

Rick bit back his anger. How could an individual who had been wronged by a mysterious, unidentified product of sophisticated technology prove that he had been injured if he had no access to the same technology that produced the toxin? How could an individual penetrate through the bureaucratic maze to avail himself of the expertise which was supposedly there for the common good? He had gone to the FDA to see if they could discover the problem and help him; now he learned that they could only help him if he told them what the problem was.

While Rick was dealing with the FDA, the symptoms persisted. The two calves that had, with Mark's help, survived the initial feeding test, were losing their hair in great patches. There was almost no hair left on their faces and necks, and there were signs that the problem was moving down their necks to the rest of their bodies. The standard ringworm treatments had failed completely; and in any case the animals' skin was more grotesquely deformed than ringworm. Within a month, the calves were virtually hairless; even the strongest preparation Dr. Jackson had prescribed had no effect. Their skin was like that of elephants; the black and white markings had faded and crumpled in the folds of the thick, coarse skin that had taken the place of their normal hide and hair.

Now the spring planting season was approaching, and Rick realized that he would have far less time to try to figure out the problem that had eluded solution during the slower winter months. With the death of each cow our financial burden increased; the dairy was after all a small business and we could little afford the constant losses we were suffering. In frustration at the death of a particularly valuable cow one day—with no unusual symptoms except adhesion of the rumen to the inside of the body cavity—Rick called the Farm Bureau Services office and unburdened himself once again to Jim McKean.

"I don't know how much longer I can take this," he began. "How would you like it if someone were to come and withdraw $900 from your bank account every day for months? That's what it's like, you know—the FBS is taking $900 from us every day. Would you lie down and take that kind of abuse? Would you watch your savings disappear, the money you saved to buy a house or a car or send your kids to school be taken away?"

"You know I can't speak for the insurance company," McKean responded evenly. "They want to find out what the problem is before they act on it. You know how cautious insurance companies are: they're not going to pay out any money until they know what it's for. They're working on it, believe me, but it takes time. They'll come up with money as soon as they prove to their satisfaction what the problem is."

It was the correct, official response, Rick realized. The financial health of an insurance company, after all, owed more to collecting premiums than to paying out claims. He regretted having sounded like one asking for mercy, but he resented hearing the same empty promises. "They're working on it," he mused bitterly. Well, so was he, but without their financial resources and while trying to run a dairy when all around seemed to be going to pieces.

It was not only the money that bothered Rick; it was the toll it was taking on everyone in other ways. He wondered how his father managed: it was not something they talked about, this agony of stewing constantly over the downhill course of things on the farm. The older man seemed to be so steady and taciturn; Rick wondered whether he burned and ached inside too. Rick knew that his younger brother felt the strain. During the time he had been working in the calf barn, a strong bond had grown between Mark and the young animals; he knew the personality of every calf that had come under his care. Mark's bitterness had been building quietly since the calves in the experiment had died. They had not intended the experiment to be a sacrifice; and even now Mark's face would freeze when he talked about the agony of having tried to pull the weakened young animals through and renew in them a desire to live that seemed to have been burned out from the inside. The continuing concern for the animals energized Dr. Jackson as well, but Rick thought he could detect in him, too, signs that the defeats and disappointments were beginning to wear on him. His shoulders seemed more stooped, his features were grim; and he seemed as frustrated as Rick with the secretive and foot-dragging manner with which Farm Bureau Services seemed to be approaching the whole matter. He had sent a sheaf of results from tests he had done to McKean, and had never heard any response one way or the other. Later, when Rick pressed the FBS veterinarian on the issue, McKean admitted that he had decided that the results—blood counts, SMA 12, gross pathology, and previous health history for each animal—were of no value and had thrown them away.

Most of all, both Rick and I realized the consequences all this was having for our family. Late in March, Farmers' Week, a week of activities on the MSU campus which highlight new developments in agriculture, offered a chance for a day trip to Lansing; and Rick had suggested that I ride along for a day of browsing in art galleries and bookstores while he sat in on a few seminars and looked at new equipment. But as the day drew closer, my fears of having an attack of chest pains and hyperventilation in public, of coming apart at the seams among all the strangers milling around, with nowhere to go and no one to turn to, gained the upper hand; and I suggested to Rick that he go alone—the change would do him good, but I wasn't in shape to join him.

"Why don't you just give your old roommate a call and

spend the day with her?" Rick asked from the fog of the bathroom where he was shaving.

"No, that's all right. If you do have time, why don't you check a bookstore for a couple of things I haven't been able to locate in Battle Creek."

"Any art supplies?"

"No, the paint just gets rubbery from being used so infrequently." I could see the disappointment in Rick's face, and I suspected that he blamed himself for my self-imposed exile in this old house that I had never much liked.

"Would you mind getting my briefcase from the office?" Rick interrupted my thoughts. "I've got to take that pile of production records on the countertop to Farm Bureau. They want the details of all our production for the last few years. That may take a while—so I don't know when I'll be home."

Driving to Lansing he decided to go first to the Farm Bureau office. The meeting with McKean was not one he relished, and he decided there was no point in spoiling the entire day anticipating it. Farm Bureau occupied a pleasant new building on the north side of the capital city; its lush and prosperous appearance seemed ironic to Rick, but he was determined not to let bitterness get the best of him.

Once in McKean's office Rick handed him the six-inch stack of computerized records. "Ken Jones said you asked for these," he said. "I hope everything you want is here."

McKean nodded and began flipping idly through the sheets with their millions of entries. Finally, he looked up. "I've got the formula you wanted for the #402 pelleted feed," he said, rifling through the papers on his desk. He passed a sheet across to Rick, who began immediately to read it. He did not tell the veterinarian that he had sent a sample of the pellets to a feed microscopist at the research facilities of Ralston-Purina to have it analyzed. He was wary of any information coming from FBS without independent confirmation.

"One thing I'd like to ask," Rick said. "I notice you include apple pomace in the formula. A lot of other feed companies won't touch that stuff: you've probably heard of the lawsuits in Pennsylvania that have resulted from evidence that apple pomace in cattle feed causes abortions in the cows."

"I've read that material, of course," McKean replied. "But

there is no solid evidence that apple pomace causes abortion in cattle or does any kind of harm at all. We include it in the formula for bulk and palatability. Because of the orchards in Michigan it's readily available, and the pomace we get is a by-product of apple sauce production for the baby food industry. You could hardly get a better grade by-product."

McKean seemed convinced—though he had also seemed convinced of the wholesomeness of the #402 pellets. Rick decided to pursue another line of inquiry.

"Did you see the lab report on the pesticide residues in the feed? Where do you suppose those residues come from? We've got almost the whole gamut of pesticides here, including a lot that have been taken off the market."

"Everything in that sample—and in all our feed—is within the federal government's tolerance for residues," McKean countered. "We're complying with the FDA guidelines. There's a little of all of those pesticides in everything we eat: there's just no way around that. If a farmer used DDT on his place thirty years ago, there'll be traces of it today in all his crops. It's just something we have to live with; and the best we can do is comply with FDA guidelines."

"Well, I don't understand why you're not hearing from other farmers about this feed," Rick said, introducing a question he had asked before but which had never been answered to his satisfaction. "You said there was only one farmer around Allegan who complained about a palatability problem with it. Have you heard from anyone else?"

"No."

"That seems inconceivable to me. Can we go through the records of the feed plant?"

"Sure," McKean said. He rose to get them out of a file cabinet in the back of his office. When he had spread them out on the table, they both bent over them. The name of the Yale Elevator showed up on the records several times as a distribution point for the feed.

"Where's the Yale Elevator?" Rick asked.

"In the Thumb area," McKean replied, "northwest of Port Huron."

"And you haven't heard anything from that area about the feed?"

"No. Absolutely nothing."

It was apparent that he was not going to learn anything about specific farmers from this office. Rick stared at the list, trying to fix in his mind the names of the elevators that had received the feed. He would have to find some other way to get the names of farmers who had received the #402 pellets. Meanwhile, he had one more question. "What about the magnesium oxide? What is your source for that? The feed tested low in magnesium each time it was run."

"We get it from Michigan Chemical Company in St. Louis, Michigan," McKean replied. "It's the same grade of stuff they put in antacids for humans."

"Do you consider Michigan Chemical an unimpeachable source?"

"Absolutely. If it's good enough for Maalox, it's good enough for your cows. They're the best source of mag oxide in this country."

"I don't know," Rick shook his head. "I keep coming back to that mag oxide. The only difference between our #402 and more commonly used feeds is the amount of soybean meal used and the amount of mag oxide. If the problem were in the soybean meal, wouldn't it have shown up in someone else's feed?"

But McKean was adamant. There had been no other complaints, he said, and the source for the magnesium oxide was above reproach. Rick headed for the Farmers' Week seminars still in the dark, but determined now to do his own investigation into the question of whether other farmers had been troubled by using the #402 pellets.

That evening when he got home, Rick called a neighbor, Laverne Bivens, whose brother Bill was an agricultural agent in the area where the Yale Elevator was located. When he had the agricultural agent's number, he called him to see if he could provide the names of some farmers in his area who were feeding the #402 pellets or any other FBS feed. It had been some years since the two had met, and Bill Bivens was initially surprised to learn that Rick was farming.

"I thought you had become a scientist, not a farmer," he said. "You always were running chemistry experiments and building radios in your spare time, as I recall."

Rick explained briefly the odyssey that had brought us from Midland to the farm, but he got quickly to the point of his call. "Bill, we've started a new setup in the past two years, and things were going well until September." Without going into detail about the various frustrating efforts to track down the source of our problem, he described the circumstances that had led us to conclude that FBS #402 was to blame. "Throughout the whole problem, Farm Bureau Services have steadfastly maintained that no one else has had any complaints about the feed. From other sources I've heard that a couple other farms—one in Coopersville, the other near Allegan—had some similar difficulties. I'm wondering whether you've seen any problems up there or if you know of anyone in your area who has been using the #402 pellets."

Bivens was silent for a while. Then he cleared his throat. "I know you're not the kind of person to make all of this up to conceal a management problem, Rick. I wish I could be of more help, but I've only got one name I can give you. A farmer by the name of Bob Demery was going to try the #402 with his silage this year. Let me give you his phone number."

Over the lunch hour Rick called Demery, who answered the telephone himself. Rick introduced himself and, being careful not to lead him on, asked Demery how he liked the #402 feed.

"We've had some problems with persistent infections after calving," Demery replied. "The vet can't get them to respond to antibiotics. We've never seen anything like it."

"How much of the #402 feed were you using?" Rick asked.

"A pound or two per cow," Demery answered. "That stuff is terribly expensive, so we just gave them a little of it. The elevator says that it isn't being made any more, so we haven't had any since January." The soft-spoken farmer's voice trailed off.

"Do you know of anyone else in your area who has been using the #402 feed?" Rick asked.

"There is one neighbor, Art Laupichler. Let me look up his number. At first we were having such good results from feeding the #402 that we got him interested in it as well."

Trying to conceal his excitement, Rick copied down the phone number and thanked Bob Demery. "I wish I could tell him that the answer to his problems is just around the corner," he said to me after hanging up. "Bill Bivens said that Demery's herd was very good. I can imagine that he tried the #402 on the advice of some feed salesman to give his cows some digestive help and a bit more protein. If only we had *proof* of what the problem is, we might be able to find a remedy for it."

Even in the short conversation it had been apparent that Demery was a careful and concerned dairyman, not the sort of bad manager who cuts corners hoping to save money, while forgetting how much stress a cow is under to produce both a calf and 17,000 pounds (8500 quarts) of milk in ten months of each year. But the #402 feed had been expensive; and Demery had used less of it than we had, so his problems were less severe. Like most farmers, he had taken the problem philosophically as just one of the many things that could go wrong in the dairy business.

The telephone call to Art Laupichler proved even more helpful. He had seen several of the same symptoms in his cattle as Rick had noted. "FBS #402? I sure do remember that stuff. Bob Demery had good luck with it, so I decided to try some too. On the #402 the cows dropped right down in milk production; they just weren't doing well at all."

"What about calving?" Rick asked.

"Some of the best cows were having problems with it. When I saw all of that happening, I called the local elevator here in Yale and told them something was wrong."

"What did they say?"

"The elevator people told me they'd come out and pick up the #402 feed and repay me for the milk I'd lost. Well, they did pick up the feed, but I haven't been paid for the milk yet."

Rick was stunned. All along the people at Farm Bureau Services had been trying to portray our problems as an isolated case with no parallels. Now here was someone who had complained and had had his feed picked up and compensation offered—if not paid—for lost production. His voice was trembling as he dialed the FBS office in Lansing and asked to speak to McKean.

"What do you have in your records about an Art Laupichler and a Bob Demery of Yale?" he asked.

After a brief pause the reply came: "I don't recognize either of those names."

Rick was indignant. "Laupichler claims to have fed #402 with some of the same results we had—lost production, difficult calving. So he called the Yale Elevator to complain, and they came right out to haul it away and promised to repay him for that lost milk. Demery had similar problems."

Rick waited, but there was no response. Angry now, he continued, "I guess I shouldn't be surprised—after the cover-up about the Agway calf experiment—that I wouldn't get straight answers about other complaints about the feed. Don't you people realize that this is our business—our lifeblood—that you're willing to sacrifice rather than admit a mistake?"

Instead of a reply, the telephone at the other end clicked into its cradle. As his fury wound down into sorrow, Rick determined not to trust anything the Farm Bureau Services told him in the future.

10

RAINED IN literature and art, I realized with frustration that I could be of very little help to Rick during the crisis that was engulfing us. It was not that I found the scientific detail uninteresting; what Rick talked about intrigued me. But what we needed was someone with the savvy to get through to a laboratory with the facilities to discover the meaning of those peaks that Dr. Furr had found in his tests in Ames. And for that goal I could offer little assistance.

There were still the children, of course. Too young to comprehend the disaster on the farm, they were nonetheless keenly sensitive to the fact that their father was becoming a stranger. He spent long hours at the barn—that was nothing new; but now his hours at home were often consumed with interminable telephone calls and long nights of quiet and frantic reading through various textbooks, searching for clues to what had felled the cows.

More keenly than ever I felt the burden of shielding them from those harsh realities while compensating for the attention Rick no longer had time to give them. He seemed not to notice them except when they interrupted the solitude he needed for reading; Stephanie's schoolwork he barely looked at, and her placement in a special early reading group at kindergarten elicited no excitement from him. Things were building to a head, I sensed, wishing all the while that some miracle would intervene.

One evening the children were playing on the living room floor in front of the sofa where Rick was reading a difficult industrial toxicology textbook he had borrowed from the library. As their enthusiasm had bubbled up, Rick had told them several times to quiet down so he could concentrate. When Stephanie suddenly bounded on him with the giggled suggestion "Let's wrestle!", he had had enough.

"I told you not to bother me," he yelled. "Now you're going to bed." With a swat across her backside he sent her upstairs, then turned to the two other children, who were retreating to another corner of the room with their toys.

"You two get ready for bed, too," he added threateningly. "No more playing!"

The noise brought me from the kitchen where I had been tidying up. "What's the problem?" I asked.

"Those kids have to go to bed now. I've been trying to concentrate and all of a sudden Stephanie jumped on top of me and wanted to wrestle."

With weary sarcasm I shot back, "I thought we had some kind of agreement about sharing the care of the children. All I do from seven in the morning to eight at night is change diapers and settle disputes and try to keep three small children quiet while you read or talk on the phone for hours. No wonder my nerves are shot. You haven't played with them or said more than 'Be quiet' for months."

"If you're tired of taking care of them, get a sitter and go off by yourself for a while," he said, not looking up from his book. "Nobody's stopping you."

"You still don't understand about nerves, do you? You've made no effort at all to understand that I'm *afraid* to go out, afraid I'll have another one of those attacks in public. Do you know how it feels to think you're going to die while you're standing in line at a supermarket or driving a car in traffic? Of course not—you don't even have nerves. Nothing bothers you . . . except a five-year-old child trying to get you to play with her for the first time in months."

"You're crazy!" he snorted.

"Maybe I am. Living in these circumstances would do it to anyone." Choking off tears I hurried off to get the children ready for bed. They were in the bathroom brushing their teeth, subdued, almost meek. I began to get ready for bed, too.

"Are you going to bed now?" Kristen asked, her round blue eyes very solemn.

"Yes, I think so, Kristen. I'm very sleepy. Aren't you sleepy too?" I knew that the children had overheard the last heated conversation between Rick and me, and it distressed me. We had tried very hard to avoid disagreeing in front of them. I wished that the outburst had made me feel better, and I wondered what he was thinking in the living room with his book.

Kristen pondered her sleeper feet. "I guess I'm getting sleepy."

I read the children a story, closed the book and paused. "We're going to have to try to be quieter for Daddy," I said. "Every night I'll read to you upstairs before bedtime unless there is something special on television. Daddy doesn't have time to read as much as he needs to when he's working, and the only time he can read is at home. He was angry tonight because he wants very much to get the cows all better so that he can play with you again."

"Does Daddy still like me?" Stephanie asked. The question stung, but I was secretly thankful that it had come out now, before bedtime.

"Of course Daddy loves all of us," I said. "But he's very busy all the time now."

I lay awake a long time that night, musing over the baffling problem I was having. There had been no explanation for the chest pains that had started the whole thing months ago—pains that still returned once in a while, usually at unpredictable inconvenient moments. The hyperventilation had taken weeks to get over, and I was still not sure how I had done it. Perhaps my body was getting revenge for years of apathy. Six months ago if someone had told me that I would be homebound out of the fear of having a seizure of acute anxiety in public, I would have laughed aloud. Now even the most inviting store was a potential hall of nightmares. My mind seemed to be at loose ends, like strands of cold cooked spaghetti in a pot. Nothing gripped me anymore but fear—no longer could I focus on a brilliant sunrise or on the texture of velvet or the sound of a fugue. I was particularly bothered by the fact that in order to go anywhere, I still had to take those pale yellow pills that the doctor had prescribed for the chest pains.

One of the most interesting recent additions to Rick's veterinary library was *The Physician's Desk Reference*, which he had found in a bookstore in East Lansing during his Farmers' Week visit to the campus. The next morning I pulled the heavy blue book from the shelf to see what it said about the pills the doctor had prescribed. Finding the name of the pills and of the company that produced them, I began to read. A few sentences into the text, I stopped short: "Patients taking Valium should be cautioned against driving a motor vehicle." The doctor had never told me that I shouldn't drive while taking the pills. I recalled angrily the times I had driven a car full of children to the store or to church or to the pediatrician. There was virtually no place I could go with the children without taking the car. Disturbed by such casual pill-dispensing, I decided to take action. Never again would I set foot in that doctor's office. Picking up the local telephone directory, I began to look for the name of another doctor; somehow, I would have to shake the need to take Valium before going out; and there seemed to be only one way to do that.

When Rick returned home for lunch, I broke the news to him. "I'm sorry, I just can't take this nervousness anymore. There has to be some solution for it besides the pills."

Rick had only seen me cry when I was angry or extremely frustrated; I knew how he hated it, so I had tried to sound calm, but he showed no response to what he probably thought was self-pity and walked into the living room.

I followed him. "What I'm trying to say is that I'm seriously considering changing doctors; I want someone who talks rather than dispensing pills."

"What's wrong with the doctor you have now—doesn't he talk?" he asked, his voice drained of emotion.

I laughed bitterly. "Let me tell you about a visit to his office. First you sit in the outside waiting room for forty minutes, reading old hunting and sports magazines with the old ladies who are there to have their latest aches discussed. Then, you progress to the inner waiting room, where there are newer magazines and you can watch the old ladies having their blood pressure taken. The usual stay in this room is two hours. They don't care how long they have to sit, because the nice doctor will listen to their litany for five minutes.

"I sat there, terrified of the pains in my chest for two hours—I saw the doctor for less than five minutes. He didn't take time to tell me how I could help myself not be afraid of the pains, or what they were, or how they had started. All he said was, 'It's just nerves—you'll get over it.' He didn't tell me that the pills he prescribed could be dependency-producing; he didn't even caution me about driving after I had taken them. I wasn't told how to begin to overcome the attack. 'Just nerves' can cover some pretty horrible sensations. What I needed then was a good, long talking-to and the beginning of some desensitization training—not the pills."

I spat the words out, and I seemed for the first time in weeks to have Rick's full attention. I hadn't told him before what had happened at the doctor's office: he had been so preoccupied with the cows that he glossed over my frustration and worry.

"What do you have in mind?" he asked. "I can't blame you for not going back to him. But who else can you see?"

"I called another doctor for an appointment this morning. He sounds pretty nice. I even got to speak to him on the phone instead of some sugary receptionist." I stopped to look straight at him. "He's a . . . shrink." Not knowing how Rick would respond to the thought of his wife seeing a psychiatrist, I used the slang term to protect myself. My fears had been misplaced.

"If you think that will help you get over this, it doesn't matter to me what kind of doctor he is." Rick had expected the news, had even hoped for it. He realized that I had no outlet; that this whole business had bothered me greatly and that I had just bottled it up. Not that he had actually asked me to become involved beyond answering the telephone and routing his messages; he had preferred to fight alone, as if the enemy were a wrestling opponent. But he had not realized how much I was fighting the battle in his shadow.

We told no one about the psychiatrist. I arranged an afternoon appointment while Stephanie was at school and the smaller children took naps. The neighbor lady who came in to watch them thought I was taking a class at the art center. The first session was about what I had expected. The doctor was a middle-aged man who had a penchant for fiddling with his comb while I poured out my various frustrations. I was afraid of rambling, but did; afterward, I wondered how he would be able to sort out the various strings of my monologue.

It was not until late in the second session that we got to the problem with the cows. "How long has this business problem been going on?" he asked.

"Forever!" I laughed, and then, afraid that the doctor would take me seriously, I added, "or so it seems. Actually, it began last September."

"What exactly is going wrong?" the doctor said, running his thumbnail along the teeth of the comb.

"Several things. First the cows wouldn't eat, and then their milk production halved while our costs actually went up. None of the veterinary people who saw the cattle could offer any solid explanation for the problem. We had fetal resorption in over a hundred bred animals, and difficult births in another hundred. To date, we've lost a hundred thousand dollars in lost milk production and animals that have died before their time or have had to be culled from the herd for poor performance."

If the doctor was shocked by this, he did not let on. "What do you think is the cause of the difficulty?"

"We strongly suspect that we received some commercial feed with an unknown contaminant in it. The feed has been tested by the state Department of Agriculture, and the laboratory which tested it discovered that experimental mice which were fed that feed died."

Still the doctor betrayed no emotion. "Have you contacted the feed company about this?"

"We contacted the feed company shortly after the problem was first noticed. So far they maintain that they have produced and sold us a nutritious, safe product."

The doctor looked at his watch. "I'm sorry, Mrs. Halbert, our time is up for this session. We'll continue this next week."

When I returned home, I found Rick in the living room reading. "Well, what are you accomplishing?" he asked over his chemical engineering magazine.

"I am trying a new exercise to relax my deep muscles," I said, getting down on the floor to show him. It looks deceptively simple—you just lie on the floor, stretch as hard as possible, and then relax. The part you don't see is the hardest. I have to think about every muscle and decide whether or not it's relaxed. All of this is to cure the jitters."

"Are you getting to the bottom of whatever it is that's bothering you? Maybe you have hidden aggressions," he jibed, trying to offer some comic relief.

"No, I think my problem is Lust," I teased. We hadn't really laughed about anything in months.

"Don't forget Avarice," he retorted.

"Or Gluttony," I said, feigning a jab at his broadening middle.

"Is this guy a Freudian?" Rick asked, his face suddenly serious.

"I'm really not sure. But when I said that I was afraid of snakes, he perked right up."

"Really? By the time you're an old lady—and with this guy's help—you'll probably be a snake handler." We laughed and embraced, and for a moment things almost seemed normal again.

By the next visit I had become less apprehensive about the trips to the psychiatrist. I allowed myself a good look around the little room, something I had been afraid to do on earlier visits lest the doctor interpret the wandering gaze as a pathological symptom. The acoustical tile on the ceiling was continued on the four walls—no doubt to deaden the sound, the same reason for the thick carpeting on the floor. This was a private consultation; and I wondered whether the doctor's other patients slipped in and out as furtively as I did. Never had I seen anyone else there but the receptionist; and I imagined myself a member of a silent army carefully and stealthily marching in and out of the small room at the same time every week.

From the beginning I had not been so much afraid of the doctor as uncomfortable with him and with his position as a judge of what I was thinking and saying and doing. What if I had slipped into madness without recognizing any of the signs? Would he detect paranoia in my growing frustration and resentment at the lack of help we were getting from the feed company and the various agencies we had contacted?

Now I had begun to see him as thoroughly human. Soft-voiced, slow-speaking, he was given to tics of his own. He fiddled with the comb constantly, and perhaps his steady gaze reflected his own concerns. I could not know, of course, but the thought was, in a strange way, vaguely liberating, even comforting.

My discomfort about being judged had come from being haunted by my shortcomings. I had focused my attention on them so sharply that I was not convinced of the existence of any positive attributes. In order to avoid offending anyone, I had sacrificed my own opinions and thoughts. In this fruitless attempt at silent martyrdom, I was inwardly seething with anger at both my situation and the farm problems, and unable to admit my anger even to myself. Recently I had added the image of the do-it-all super-mother, scurrying here and there to see that her children have a wealth of experience. Trying to do all of that with Rick's support would have been an incredible assignment; now that all his energy was devoted to the invisible enemy in the feed, the task was impossible.

"I want to talk about getting off the tranquilizers," I told the doctor.

For the first time, he allowed himself a smile. "I'm very pleased with your progress, Mrs. Halbert. You realize now that you've become emotionally dependent on them; and that's the first step to freeing yourself from that dependency."

When I returned home that afternoon, I talked to the babysitter longer than usual. When Stephanie returned from school, I made the offer: "Let's drive in for some ice cream." The children scurried for their jackets, and I looked at the small vial of pale yellow pills. Instead of taking one, I tucked them into the deepest corner of my purse and ushered the children into the car.

It was the first time since the chest pains began that I had been farther away than the woods a half mile from the house without taking one of the pills. The one-mile trip to the store passed without event until we arrived and had to wait for an elderly gentleman who seemed to be laying in a year's supply of food all at once. A minor delay, but it had never taken much to trigger the feeling of panic. The familiar light-headed feeling seized me, and I forced myself to look away from the slow old man and his cases of canned goods. My eyes found the label of a prepared food product, and I read the words very slowly to myself, concentrating on each one and on its possible shades of meaning. The children were milling about, tugging on my skirt—"Please, Momma, can I have a licorice whip?" "Can I have some candy?" "Can I have a popsicle?"

The old man was counting out what appeared to be all of the money he had onto the counter. "I will not panic. I will not panic. I will not panic," I repeated to myself. I looked up; the old man was leaving with his cases of food. It was our turn now, and I had overcome the lightheadedness and the fear. It was only a mile away from the house, and only a small store, but it was a start.

When Rick came home, I told him quietly, "We went to the general store this afternoon, and I didn't take the pills." He looked down at me and smiled. I doubted if he really understood what a great victory it was for me, but I rejoiced inside anyway.

Every day I took the children for a ride, every day a little farther from home. Soon I stopped taking the little vial of tranquilizers in my purse. Finally, we went to a large supermarket—one where we would be sure to have a wait in line. Everything went well until we reached the checkout desk, and the old fear struck. This time, it was punctuated by the throat-grabbing chest pains. This is not the ideal place to have a full attack, I told myself. I could feel my cheeks redden, as I struggled for composure. I concentrated on the children—on their remarkable china-doll fair skin, on Kristen's curling auburn hair and round, bright blue eyes, on Lisa's fine wispy strawberry-blond hair and hazel blue eyes, on Stephanie's thick brown hair and blue-gray eyes. Normally one hoped for peace and quiet from children in the supermarket; now I found myself almost hoping that they would do something to get my mind off the chest pains. I would have been grateful, so I thought, if they had knocked over a display at that moment. But somehow we got through the checkout line and into the car with the groceries. I began to shake, and took a deep breath. I had to get them all home again. Then I realized that the pains had stopped.

The visits to the doctor would continue, sometimes obviously helpful, sometimes only discouraging. I wished that he would show more evident concern with the injustice of the whole problem with the cattle, but Rick attributed his aloofness on that score to "professional manner." In any case, there were some noticeable improvements in my psyche, and after the downhill slide of the last six months, that was a lot to be thankful for.

There were no medals for the battle, no awards or ribbons except those you made for yourself. The children didn't seem to know that I had to fight a battle each time we went to the store or to church or went for ice cream; and after a while, Rick didn't seem to care. I wondered what happened to those who could not bring themselves to face their enemy—the silent, drab people who didn't go to war within themselves.

11

APRIL MEANT spring planting and for most farmers the ancient hopefulness of anticipating the harvest even while seeding the soil. We had decided to plant eight hundred acres of corn this year—which meant fourteen-hour days seven days a week during late April and May. Once the corn was in, it would be nearly time for the first cutting of hay, and since Karl had not been replaced, the men would be busier than ever the next few weeks.

Rick felt defeated and drained from his struggle with the feed company and the bureaucracy. Now he even had to face the prospect of losing all that he and his family had worked two generations to achieve. When he was young his father and grandfather had had two farms making up fewer than three hundred acres of choppy, partially wooded land. By taking calculated risks and working hard, they had consolidated smaller holdings into one large farm. From fewer than fifty cows in milk, they had grown to a setup for five hundred. A new two-hundred-cow barn had been built, but it stood nearly empty during the past four months, when they had projected that it would be full.

Some vague hints from FBS renewed the hope that an insurance settlement would be just around the corner; with that in mind, Rick had virtually dropped the idea of spending any more of his own time and money on research into the feed problem. The efforts to find a mass spectrometer had not been successful. Before abandoning the pursuit entirely, however,

Rick learned from a veterinarian in Iowa the name of one more government research station that might study the feed—this one in College Station, Texas. A pregnancy toxicologist by the name of Harry Smalley took Rick's call and sounded very interested in the problem he outlined.

"The animals went down before calving and seemed to lose the will to live?" Dr. Smalley mused. "And cows showed no adjustments of their pelvic ligaments or udders before difficult labor? These are strange symptoms—like nothing I've ever encountered."

"That's correct," Rick said.

"Would you be able to send some of the feed down here? I'd like to set up an experiment using some pregnant ewes."

Despite the number of times he had been burned when false hopes were kindled, Rick was impressed by Smalley's interest. **122** For the first time he had encountered someone who seemed interested in the problem right away.

"Why don't you call Dr. Scott, the USDA vet, in Lansing," Dr. Smalley suggested, "and have him obtain a government bill of lading to ship five hundred pounds of the feed down here?"

Elated, Rick drove out to the barn where the remaining #402 pellets were stored. The green mound had shrunk visibly from the constant inconclusive sampling. As he shoveled the pellets into two cardboard drums he wondered whether he was finally doing this for the last time. That afternoon a call came from Dr. Scott.

"I don't understand why, Mr. Halbert," he began apologetically, "but my request for a government bill of lading was denied by my supervisor in Ohio. I've never had this happen before."

Rick sighed wearily. He wondered if every institution was determined to impede his progress on the problem. He had lost track of how much money he had invested in the still-fruitless search, but he was certain that shipping costs from our farm to Texas would not add significantly to that amount. It was the principle that grated at him. "All right, Dr. Scott. Thanks for trying. I guess I'll contact a freight company and ship it myself."

Before the day was over the drums were on a truck for the

Southwest. The freight bill was $45. By the end of June, we hoped to receive some results from Dr. Smalley's tests.

While we awaited news from Texas and from the insurance company, preparations for spring planting moved ahead. Gordon, the mechanic, spent days working on the huge plow and disc harrow, greasing and tightening and checking weak spots and replacing worn points and bolts. Death still haunted the barns, an inevitable feature of life on a farm, but one that Rick, like most farmers, could never just shrug off.

Some of the deaths were harder to take than others. Number 689 was the best animal we had ever bred, by common consent. As a two-year-old she had set a state record in butterfat production, and we had been hoping her progeny would carry on her outstanding traits. "Supercow," the men called her, but she looked anything but super now lying in the maternity stall where she had calved a week ago.

"You'd better go have a look at 689," Mark said as he lifted a can of colostrum from the truck bed. I don't think there's a whole lot of hope, but see what you think."

Rick grabbed his box of veterinary supplies and walked into the center of the barn with his younger brother. Mark was carrying the nursing bottles for the young calves, Rick the depleted collection of medications with which they had tried to reverse the decline of "Supercow."

The cow made no effort to rise as they swung open the gate to the stall. She lay upright, propped against two straw bales, but her neck was outstretched as if her head was too heavy to hold up. Her large eyes were sunk deep and the mass of her skull was obvious as it protruded around them. There was no fever, no tearing, no cud. She was simply starving—and going downhill fast. If a sick cow stayed down too long, death was certain. Rick and Mark tried to get the emaciated animal to her feet, but they were no match for her dead weight. With each effort they made, the cow heaved mightily, foundered, stretched out on her side, and extended her thin neck. "We'd better get some help," Mark muttered.

With four men and the help of a rope attached to the bucket of the small tractor, they finally pulled the cow to her feet. Pathetically thin, she bore little resemblance to the proud animal in her identifying photograph in our registered cow file. Her coat was dull and hair was missing in patches on her face and neck. For an hour Rick stayed with the cow trying to get her to move. But her will to live was ebbing, and there was no way he knew to give her the desire to fight back.

The cow finally dropped to her knees again, crumpled into a breathing heap of hide and bone in the corner of the stall. Rick braced her with straw bales so that she couldn't roll over onto her side, scratched her poll sadly, and walked out with his useless veterinary supplies.

"How is she?" Mark asked, looking up from the two baby calves he was feeding.

"Let's check her in a few hours," Rick said. "I don't think it will be long now."

One of the calves that Mark had not yet fed was tottering after the nursing bottle in his hand. Rick looked down at it. There was something wrong with the calf: it seemed to aim for the bottle, but always missed it. A normal calf could find the bottle with its eyes closed every time. This one blundered into the other calves and into the side of the pen. Over and over it tried to reach the bottle in Mark's hand, and over and over it missed. Mark caught the calf and forced the bottle into its mouth, but it did not begin to suck: it seemed to be missing some of the basic elements of the survival instinct. A chill ran through Rick as he noticed that the calf bore the same markings as the cow he had just left in the stall—"Supercow."

Mark saw the look on Rick's face. "It's some kind of brain damage," he said quietly. "I was waiting for a better time to tell you. . . ."

That night Number 689 died; her calf survived her by two days.

On a warm Saturday in April Mark had a well-earned day off, and Rick decided to take the children along when he went to feed the calves. That particular aspect of farming was still a treat for the children, but Rick was reluctant at this point to make it a regular chore for them, lest he destroy their love for the land—like so many other farmers he had seen—by exposing them too early to the drudgery of the business. It was a chance to spend some time with the children, and a time for them to get away from the house, and those things more than compensated for the tendency of the three to overfeed the calves, particularly the ones nearest to the grain storage bin.

When they reached the calf barn, he swung each child down from the truck cab in turn. He enjoyed trying to prick their curiosity by making up nonsense songs and riddles for them to figure out. When words would not do, he cuddled or swung them. He had once been uneasy around small children—as he was with unfamiliar adults—but with his own children he was comfortable and relaxed. In the intimate surroundings of the open field or his own house he even allowed himself to be silly and childlike as he played with them. That had not been very often lately, he reflected soberly.

"Lisa, you can stay in the barn as long as you want, but you have to obey the rules. When you're tired of visiting the calves, you go up to Grandma's house."

Stephanie had already gone into the barn and was scooping grain from the barrel. Rick wondered whether diarrhea in any of the calves tomorrow would give Mark a clue to who had assisted at the feeding. Kristen helped Rick with the bottle-feeding of the younger calves. In its enthusiasm a calf nearly bowled her over, and Rick smiled as she tried to figure out a way to hold the bottle with only one hand while petting the calf with the other. It was a slow way to feed a hundred bawling calves, Rick mused as he caught glimpses of the children, caught up in their fascination with the young animals, but it was well worth it. When the job was finished the children were reluctant to leave until Rick suggested that they go visit the pond and the swans his father raised. The elder Halbert had always kept birds as a hobby; there were a few bantam hens around, and each spring he would carry a clutch of warm duck or pheasant eggs to the nest of one of the hens and fool her into brooding the young orphan birds. Racing pigeons wheeled overhead, purple martins swooped in and out of their houses, swans glided in the pond he had made by damming up the creek, and even the barn swallows had been allowed to nest in the garage.

At the pond, Rick showed the children how to call the graceful white cob, challenging him to a show of supremacy over the pond. Despite cautionary stories Rick had told the children about the powerful wings of a swan, which are capable of delivering a karate-like blow, they were unafraid of the big white birds. He gave the swans their ration of grain, and Lisa drizzled grain from the bucket in a twisted thread of a path, trying to get the birds closer to her.

"They won't come up to you, Lisa," Rick said. "They're not very good at moving around on dry land, and they don't want to be caught out of water." Lisa was undeterred. Kristen and Stephanie had found some willow boughs that had fallen from the tree by the pond, and they were thrashing noisily in the water by the edge of the pond. Taking pity on the agitated birds, Rick called the children to him. Sending the children off for a visit at his mother's house, just up the long hill from the pond, he walked over to the shed where the six-month-old calves were kept to feed them. When that was completed, he turned his attention to the bull pen calves.

126   There were only two calves left from the experiment that had provided the first solid clue to the poisonous nature of the #402 feed pellets. As Rick rounded the corner of the barn into the bull pen, something seemed strange, but he disregarded the feeling until he got to the bottom of the stairway in the manger area. One of the last two calves was stretched out on the dirt floor of the pen; and the other calf with it was acting strange, as if it sensed that something was wrong.

As Rick approached the pen, he saw no heaving in the calf's rib cage, and he knew at once why the second calf would not go near it. Sensing death, the other animal had pulled away from its companion and stood in confusion. Walking into the pen, Rick examined the dead calf. There were no signs that its death had been agonizing; the dirt floor of the pen was not torn up by thrashing hooves. Apparently it had simply stretched out and given up the fight with the internal demons that the feed had unleashed upon it.

A small noise interrupted Rick's examination. He turned to see Stephanie, who had slipped quietly down the stairs and was standing wide-eyed at the gate of the pen. Rick was not prepared for the child: she was clearly aghast at the sight of the calf, but he did not know what to say or do or how to approach her feelings about it.

"What happened to the calf, Daddy? Why is it lying down?" she asked very quietly.

"The calf was very sick, Stephanie," he replied uncertainly. "So sick that it died."

She reached out toward the dead calf, then drew back in confusion as the living calf had. Rick put his arm around her. "It won't ever be able to run or jump or eat or sleep again. It won't ever hurt again either." He let her get used to the sight of the very still calf. Finally he stood up and said, "We have to get it out of the pen so we can bury it." Reaching down, he caught two of the calf's legs and began to drag it toward the gate. "Can you open the gate for me, Stephanie?"

When he had the dead calf in the open space at the base of the stairway Rick stopped dragging it. "We can't bury it here," Stephanie said with sudden alarm.

"We're not going to bury it right away," Rick said. "I want Dr. Jackson to have a look at it to see if he can figure out why it died." They finished caring for the living calf and closed the **127** gate to its pen. As they walked by the carcass, Rick watched his daughter recoil from any contact with it. He said quietly, "The calf isn't much different from the ones you fed this morning, is it? It has all of its parts except for its hair. Are you afraid of it because it's so still or are you afraid of the way it looks?"

She shook her head, unable to put her feelings into words. Rick continued, "I don't know why the calf lost its hair or why its skin looks so strange. It looks like an elephant, doesn't it?"

"Was the calf very sick, Daddy?" she asked.

"Yes," he said, "but not the way you get sick. The calf ate something that was very bad for it, and that made it so sick that it finally died. Maybe it was better for the calf to die than for it to be so sick that we couldn't help it get better."

"I guess so," she said, unconvinced. She had been so certain that he could fix anything, that he could make sick cattle get better, that the discovery that some things were beyond his power was, in a way, a bigger shock than the sight of the dead calf. She had heard her parents and grandparents and the farm-hands speak of dead animals, but the sight of this calf had brought all that home.

To try to ease the shock and give her a more balanced point of view, Rick brought Stephanie back to the calf barn, where she could see the younger calves she had been feeding and petting an hour earlier. As she rumpled the fur of one of them,

Rick said, "This calf isn't sick. See how happy it is to have you here to visit? Look at the fur on it—does it look like the fur on the calf we took out of the pen?"

"That calf didn't have any fur," Stephanie retorted. "It was . . . bald!" They looked around the barn one last time, and went to get the other two children to return home for lunch.

In mid-April Rick decided to call the Michigan Department of Agriculture to see whether we could vaccinate the calves for dairy replacement against Bang's disease at two months instead of the more customary three to six months. Dr. Whitehead, the veterinarian at the Department of Agriculture, said that he had read the reports on early vaccinations as well and that the department was looking into the possibility of approving them within a few months, but that for the present, we would have to continue the regular schedule. Just as the conversation was about to close, the veterinarian lowered his voice. "Did you say you're from around Battle Creek?" he asked.

"Yes, our farm is a bit north of there," Rick replied.

"Have you contacted the FDA in Detroit recently?"

"Yes, we contacted them about a problem we had with some dairy feed we bought from Farm Bureau Services." Rick was uneasy at the mention of the Food and Drug Administration: what reason would the Michigan Department of Agriculture have to know about his contact with them?

"A few weeks ago, while I was in a meeting with a legislative committee, I was called out to discuss something urgent with an FDA representative. He said that we at the Department of Agriculture should withhold your milk from the market because there was lead in it."

Rick was flabbergasted. No one had told him anything like that; indeed, his every effort to find out anything from the FDA had met with failure. No wonder he had been advised to stay away from them. "Well, what did you do?" he asked.

"We went into our records of your milk samples. We found that we had tested your milk for lead and other heavy metals last fall and that we had found nothing. So we notified the FDA in Detroit that your milk samples contained no lead. They said OK and took our word for it. The matter was dropped."

Rick thanked Dr. Whitehead for the information. So this was the bottom line of the investigation that had started with Clarence Bozarth's diligent sample-collecting. After taking all those samples, they seemed to prefer to operate on presumption—the sketchy information he had given them just to get them interested in the problem. Apparently they had not even tested the milk sample in their laboratory and had relied on the Michigan Department of Agriculture test done months earlier. His scheme to interest the FDA in their problem had almost ended in their exclusion from the milk market without coming one step closer to the solution.

From Louis Newman, a veterinarian at Michigan State, Rick now learned of a US Department of Agriculture laboratory in Beltsville, Maryland, which might have the facilities and manpower to analyze the feed and identify the latent peaks Dr. Furr had noticed. Newman gave Rick the name of a Dr. Smith, and Rick was soon on the telephone again, half hopeful, half expecting the usual brushoff.

"What I need, Dr. Smith, is someone who has the interest and ability to use a mass spectrometer to identify toxic materials," Rick said after he had outlined the cattle problems.

"Well, we have two men here who might be able to help you, Mr. Halbert," Dr. Smith responded. "Dr. Bittman and Dr. Fries both work in the area of pesticides. Why don't you try to get in touch with one of them?"

There was a short delay, since both of the men were in California attending a conference, but late in April Rick made another telephone call. Dr. George Fries listened sympathetically to Rick's description of the feed problem and his plea for help in identifying the toxin. Rick left him a list of five references, urging that he call them for an independent opinion from veterinarians and researchers who had worked on the problem so far.

A few days later Rick called him back. "Any luck in contacting someone on my list?" he asked.

"Yes. One of the men on the list is an old college friend of mine, whose judgment I trust, so I called him first."

Something about the measured way Fries was speaking hinted to Rick that he was trying to let him down gently. "Well?" he asked.

"It was the opinion of the person I spoke with that you are having a problem with a mold toxin. That's not in my area, I'm afraid. Since I work with residues left by man-made material, I can't really help you."

Shaken as he was, Rick was not about to give up at this point without an extra effort. "Could you please call some of the others on the list?" he asked. "Don Hughes, for instance, who is on the list, found that the peaks didn't contain sulphur or phosphorus, but based on electron-capture gas liquid chromatography he discovered that the peaks are halogenated and have a high molecular weight. I'm convinced that we *are* dealing with a man-made material."

Fries realized the point Rick was trying to make; with only a couple of exceptions, halogens appeared in man-made organic compounds.

"By the way," Rick added, "may I ask whom you did call?"

"Don Hillman. I knew him at school, and I thought that he would be up-to-date on your situation."

"Don did take some samples from our total spectrum of feeds rather early into the problem, but he found nothing when he tested them for mold. Later, we sent samples of the feed to Dr. Pier at NADL to have him test it for mold—and he also found nothing. He turned it over to Dr. Al Furr of NADL; he's the one I'd like you to call: he found the peaks I had hoped you'd be able to identify. I'm sure that after you talk to him you'll be convinced that we don't have a problem with a mold toxin here."

Rick's persistence paid off. Dr. Fries agreed to try calling more of the men on the list; and the one contact we had with a possible solution to the mystery of the peaks was kept alive. The fact was enough to lighten the burden of wondering about the problem for a few days more. On the last Wednesday in April, Rick called Fries back. This time, the scientist was enthusiastic; his curiosity had been awakened by the conversations he had with the other investigators. "I'll send you a sample of the feed by special delivery," Rick said, and the sample was in the mail the same afternoon.

On Friday Rick called Jim McKean to check how FBS-sponsored research at WARF was going. "We've found out that the halogen is bromine," McKean reported. Rick was surprised. He had expected that they would find chlorine, not bromine, because chlorine was used far more often than bromine in industrial chemicals. The presence of bromine indicated a special-use material. His curiosity piqued, Rick asked, "Can you give me the molecular weights of the peaks?"

"The material has two major peaks and five minor peaks," McKean said. "You might want to take down the molecular weights of the major peaks. That's all the information I have." He read the figures off to Rick.

Nearly bursting with the news Rick called Dr. Fries in Beltsville. "WARF has discovered that the material is bromine. The chromatogram has two major peaks and five minor peaks." As Rick read the molecular weights that McKean had given him, Dr. Fries repeated each one and then paused.

"That sounds like something I've run before," he said. "A fire retardant. Let me just check my files a minute." Over the sound of his own racing heartbeat Rick could hear some papers rustling. Then, "Okay, let me read these molecular weights back to you to check." Fries read back the numbers once more, slowly and distinctly.

"I got this material as a sample from a chemical company. They had advertised a new fire retardant in the trade magazine *Chemical Week*, and Dr. Bittman ordered a sample to run, mostly out of curiosity I guess. The trade name of the stuff is 'Firemaster BP-6.' Chemically, it's basically polybrominated biphenyl, PBB."

"What companies manufacture PBB?" Rick asked.

"I got this sample from Michigan Chemical Company in St. Louis."

The missing piece fell into place. "That solves the riddle!" Rick interjected excitedly. "Our feed was supposed to have magnesium oxide added to it, and the feed company got their mag oxide from Michigan Chemical. We hadn't been able to account for the low test for magnesium in the feed; what apparently happened was that Michigan Chemical sent the wrong stuff to the Farm Bureau and the fire retardant was added to our feed in place of mag oxide."

With the caution of the trained scientist, Dr. Fries said, "Well, I don't have your feed sample yet, so I can't state positively that PBB is in it, but it certainly looks like it. I'll give you a call when I run a test on the feed itself and let you know."

Although the identification was tentative, Rick was convinced that PBB was the source of their difficulties. Searching for more information on the chemical, Rick called the home office of the firm, located in Chicago since a merger. He found himself talking to a Mr. Garman in the marketing department. "Mr. Garman, we've just identified a material that has apparently been added, inadvertently, to our cattle feed in place of magnesium oxide. The material is Firemaster BP-6, manufactured by your company."

There was an audible gasp from the other end, but Rick continued. "I'd like to know exactly how toxic Firemaster BP-6 is."

Garman left the phone to hunt for the data the company had compiled on the toxicity of the fire retardant. When he returned he read the research summary to Rick. "Firemaster BP-6, hexabromobiphenyl, is classified as non-toxic by ingestion or dermal application, is not a primary skin irritant or corrosive material, is not an eye irritant, and is not highly toxic by inhalation exposure. To determine if the sample is toxic by inhalation exposure would require testing at a concentration of 200 mg/liter. The known LD50 is 21.5 grams per kilogram." LD50 is the dose at which half the test animals will die.

As soon as he had finished his conversation with Mr. Garman, Rick called Farm Bureau Services veterinarian Jim McKean. "I've found out what the contaminant in the feed is," he reported. "Dr. Fries at Beltsville identified the material as being a fire retardant called Firemaster BP-6, manufactured by Michigan Chemical Company. I'll call you back next week, when the confirmation is complete."

The telephone call with Dr. Fries was on Monday, the next working day. There was no lingering over small talk. "I ran your sample this morning and compared it with the Firemaster chromatogram. There's no doubt about it: the peaks in your feed are the chemical fingerprints of polybrominated biphenyl. I hope I haven't created a problem for you, but I felt that it was my duty to call the US Department of Agriculture and tell them that there might be a contamination problem in Michigan."

12

AY BEGAN with a lifting of our spirits. Now that the contaminant was no longer a phantom but an identifiable chemical compound, Rick began to relax for the first time in months. Finally we thought that we could see some hope for the cattle and the economic future of the farm. Rick's contacts with Farm Bureau Services revealed that FBS personnel were in much the same mood as he—something approaching euphoria seemed to reign at FBS now that the origin of the plague had been shifted to the Michigan Chemical Company.

Twice during that first week in May someone came to take milk samples—one a representative of the Michigan Department of Agriculture laboratory, the other representing the Food and Drug Administration. The two visits did not particularly worry Rick; he imagined that the FDA was going to compare the current sample with the samples Mr. Bozarth had taken in March and the one the MDA had taken earlier.

One sunny day in mid-May I had settled down in the office to do some reading. The mild weather had not been enough to keep the children playing outdoors, and they were running through the house in mad pursuit of each other, their yells and laughter muffled just enough by the closed door to allow me a modicum of concentration. Then even that was broken by the ringing of the telephone in the kitchen.

With a shout over the hubbub for quiet, I picked up the receiver. "Mrs. Halbert, is Rick there?" The voice was vaguely familiar.

"No, I'm sorry. He's out plowing. May I take a message?" A crash came from the living room and three once-small voices hollered, "The cheetah's escaped! Get the cheetah!"

I apologized into the phone and tried to calm the children, who were completely oblivious to anyone else, much less a scolding mother. "I'm sorry, I can't hear you over the noise in here. Can I tell Rick who called?"

"This is Ken Van Patten," the voice answered, and I recognized immediately that it was the State dairy division man. "It's really very important that I speak with Rick before the milk hauler comes today."

"Couldn't I take a message to him?" I shouted over the din.

"No, I'm afraid I have to tell him myself. The news isn't good, and I know he'll have some questions."

I felt my legs going weak and the tension building up in a tight band of muscles circling my head as I mechanically wrote down a telephone number where Rick could reach Ken. As I hung up the phone, the cheetah hunters raced past, and I reached out blindly for the likeliest perpetrator among the principals. "Why can't you kids be quiet when I'm on the phone?" I screamed. "That was a very important telephone call, and you were so noisy I could hardly hear the man!" In a burst of frustration, brought on as much by foreboding as by the children's misbehavior of the last few minutes, I whirled the wide-eyed girl around and whacked her across the backside. She stumbled and fell to her knees against the grill of the cold-air register. The sight of blood from a small cut in her knee put an immediate end to the frolicsome mood of all three children, but it set off a round of forlorn wailing in Stephanie.

Regretting my loss of temper, I bandaged the knee and tried to comfort her as long as I dared; Ken Van Patten had sounded very urgent over the telephone. Piling the three children into the car, I drove over to the distant field where Rick was plowing. I waved him down, climbed up onto the large tractor, and gave him the message. In my rage over the children's noise I had avoided—repressed, perhaps—thinking about why Van Patten had said he wanted to talk to Rick before the milk hauler came. No such escape from the facts offered itself to Rick. Silently he shut off the engine and walked with me to the car. Wordlessly we drove home. I stayed outside with the children while Rick made the telephone call whose purpose both of us had guessed.

His face was grim when he emerged from the house a few minutes later. "We've been shut off," he said abruptly. "I've got to drive to the barn to stop Pete Schrantz from picking up the milk."

As he drove toward the barn, Van Patten's words kept coming back to Rick in painful shards. "I'm sorry, Rick," Van Patten had begun—Rick remembered that he had felt the first flash of despair when the message had come draped with apology. "I'm going to have to ask that you not ship your milk today." Van Patten had continued quietly, as the apprehension spread through Rick's body. Rick had a hard time drawing enough breath to reply to him: it seemed as if someone had crushed his chest, driving all of the air out of his lungs. "We've found a substantial amount of PBB in your milk— 40 parts per million." When Van Patten had finished his message, Rick had gasped for his answer; he had no choice but to comply. It was not Van Patten's job to prescribe or suggest what the state expected us to do with the milk that could not be shipped, or with the cattle that produced it. His paramount responsibility was to cut off the contamination as soon as possible.

Now the race was against the milk hauler. The agriculture department did not have the time to send an inspector out immediately to remove the permit to ship milk from the wall of the milkhouse. Until they did Rick would have to act as his own inspector, turning the hauler away, and thereby cutting all of us off from the only source of income we had. The sale of milk supported us and Rick's parents and brother, and the families of our five employees.

When Rick arrived at the barn, he saw that the milk hauler had not come yet. Standing in the clean-scrubbed milkhouse he looked up at the two bulk storage tanks—they had 8,000 quarts of milk ready to go—cooled, agitated, waiting for someone to open the tank and let it escape. Rick simply could not bring himself to open the drain and let the milk run out of the tank into the floor drain; instead, he climbed the ladder and looked down into the larger tank. The milk swirled lazily, looking as innocent and pure as ever. There was no way of seeing the PBB in the milk, though Rick knew now that the agent that had felled so many cows had also gotten into their milk. Carefully capping the tank, Rick climbed back down the ladder and went into the barn office to wait for the hauler.

Mark came into the office, looking for a thermometer. Rick looked up from the desk. "You'd better sit down. I just talked to Ken Van Patten; he said that they've found PBB in the milk. We're shut off."

"God!" Mark said softly. "Did you tell Dad yet?"

"First I have to tell Pete not to pick up the milk; MDA requested that we tell the hauler we're shut off until they send an inspector out to pull our permit. Look, if you see Dad, ask him to come up here—unless you want to tell him yourself."

"I think you better do it—you're the one who talked with Van Patten," Mark said, and then asked, "What are we supposed to do now? Did Van Patten say what we're supposed to do with the milk?"

"There was no word on that—they're primarily interested in cutting off the sources of the contaminant. I guess that we'll have to drain the milk into the holding area waste tank and haul it out with the manure tank."

Mark left the barn office as shaken as Rick had been when he had come from his phone call. As Rick sat at the desk, staring at the traffic flowing by on the highway, he wondered if this was some awful mistake. Occasionally, he glanced at the telephone beside him, half expecting Van Patten to call back and release him from his agony. But no phone call came.

When Pete Schrantz pulled the milk truck onto the concrete driveway in front of the milkhouse, Rick went out to the truck to tell Pete that they were not going to ship milk that day. The hauler was stunned: "They called you just this morning? I've never seen anything like this—it's so sudden. I've lost two big stops this morning, and I've only gone to six farms. If this keeps up, I won't have enough milk to make the trip!"

Schrantz was usually cheerful and talkative, but today he was uncharacteristically silent. He knew that he would only be paid for the milk that could be sold. Driving an empty truck to Detroit every day would bankrupt him.

When the milk truck pulled out of the driveway, Rick went back into the milkhouse, and stood looking at the large grey bulk storage tank full of milk. It seemed as if he had awakened to a nightmare and could not shake himself of its consequences. One simple telephone call, and all of the industry of two lifetimes was shut down, as if a giant hand had come and switched off a light. Kneeling on the concrete floor of the milk-house, he checked the floor drain beneath the bulk tank, then opened the drain. The precious white liquid flowed onto the floor and swirled into the square floor drain. Rick stood, watching it disappear, knowing that it was the farm and our lifeblood that was running into the ground.

The men felt obligated to keep milking the cows, even though all the milk had to be drained into the waste tank; it was hard to admit defeat and stop all the work rhythms that had sustained them. Rick spent hours in the barn office trying to think his way out of the cage he had unwittingly constructed while he was trying to name the poison in the feed. He was sleeping very badly now, and the consequences of nights of half-sleep pursuing enigmas showed up all day long. On the other side of the bed, I struggled with my nerves, stretching and relaxing aching muscles sometimes dozens of times before sleep finally overtook me.

One night Rick, after trying to go to sleep for hours, asked where I kept the tranquilizers.

"Are you sure that you know what you're doing?" I asked anxiously, recalling the grip the pale yellow pills had, and angry with myself for not having thrown them away when I needed them no longer. We had been talking in the dark, trying to chip away at the disaster, trying to make some sense of the situation the quarantine had thrust on us.

"All I want to do is sleep," Rick said tensely. "I haven't slept more than a few hours a night since the quarantine began. There's no end to this thing. Every day more farms are added. My mother is getting so depressed doing our bookkeeping that Dad says he finds her in tears when he comes home to eat: money is just running through the account like water through a sieve."

"Has the Department of Agriculture said anything definite?" I asked.

"I called them yesterday, trying to get an answer to that question. They have had a bill introduced in the legislature that would condemn the quarantined cattle. They would in effect buy the tainted cows and pay the farmer for them when they were hauled away. The cattle would go to a site where they would be humanely destroyed and buried; and the farmers would have money to settle mounting overdue bills and begin cleaning the farm up. Then the Department would go to court against Farm Bureau Services and Michigan Chemical to recover the money it would cost to run the program and the kill site."

"Do you think it will pass?"

"Well, the legislature is also considering an education bill right now, and of course the teachers' groups want that funding approved before the next school year. If that passes in its present form, the state treasury will be nearly dry. With this being an election year no legislators are going to risk looking like spendthrifts. The Detroit papers are editorializing to let the MDA-sponsored bill die in committee. What are thirty farms, after all?" he added bitterly.

"Detroit!" I said bitterly. I had grown up around the state's largest city, but now it seemed somehow on this hopeless, sleepless night to symbolize the enemy. To the mind of the average citizen the economic health of Michigan meant simply how well the automobile industry was doing. What indeed were thirty farms?

"Well," Rick said grimly, "until somebody comes up with a plan, we're going to have to scrape along. Maybe we can get more loans from the bank to pay our bills and try to clean the place up, but with things the way they are now, it would be difficult to convince a bank that we're a sound loan prospect—who knows if we'll still be in business when the time comes for the first payment?" He paused. "Do you think we can get by on our savings account for a while? Dad and I agreed to stop drawing pay from the business until this thing gets settled. I can't ask the men to work without pay, and I hate to let any of them go."

"We'll manage," I said, "I hope."

The next morning Rick took yet another look at the pile of bills that outlined the bare bones of the dairy business: payroll, feed, fuel for trucks and tractors, parts for equipment, veterinary bills, utilities payments, mortgage payments. The only way to pay the bills and keep going was to sell milk, and eight thousand quarts of that commodity were swirling down the drain every day. It was no surprise when he did the calculations again: we were going backward in double time. He sat at the desk drained of energy, his senses dull from lack of sleep, his stomach in knots. He tried the relaxing exercises I had learned from the doctor, but peace was elusive.

One small hope was offered by the possibility that the cows would eliminate the chemical from their systems. Rick called Dr. Fries to ask whether he had done any tests concerning this. The scientist reported some evidence that the amount would halve in about eight weeks, but he cautioned Rick that his evidence came from tests on animals with low exposures and shouldn't be generalized to the whole situation without further testing. Beyond that there were no tests of the PBB and its effects.

Slim hope was better than no hope at all, Rick reasoned. The report from Dr. Fries was enough to sustain him for a few weeks. The cows ranged from 500 to 1000 parts per million of PBB in their bodies. If the material halved every eight weeks, it seemed likely that enough of it would have left their systems in a year to make the milk legally salable. That was enough hope to go on, at least until the next Department of Agriculture tests were run. **139**

Disposal of the tainted milk soon became a problem as well. The waste tank in the holding area was soon full of a foul-smelling combination of milk, wash water, and manure, and neighbors had begun to complain of the stench when the wind changed. Rick decided to haul the waste and milk out and spread it on the fallow fields, but once the load got into the field, everything seemed to go wrong. The loaded tank got bogged down in the field and had to be drained on the spot before it could be pulled loose from the mud that imprisoned it. The stinking mixture was allowed to run off, following the contours of the cornfield bordering the lane, and disappeared into the young stand of corn.

Within a few days, we noticed that the corn in the field where the tank had drained had fallen flat, as though someone had driven a steamroller through that part of the field. Rick began to worry. It might have been the lactic acid in the milk that took the starch out of the corn, he thought, but it might also have been yet another contamination by PBB. After discussing the problem with the Department of Agriculture, Rick decided to rent a tank truck from the milk hauler, and each day

Mark would use it to carry the tainted production of that milking out to the most inaccessible part of the farm to dump it among a stand of scrawny hardwood trees. Within a week, the leaves on the bushes in the woodlot had begun to yellow and wilt.

"Let's remember never to remove those trees for extra pasture," Mark said to Rick as he pointed to the effect on the undergrowth.

"I don't think we'll forget," Rick said solemnly.

Just before the quarantine had been issued, we had sent two cows which were low producers to the slaughterhouse. It is a common practice on dairy farms to slaughter for home use healthy animals whose milk production made it uneconomical to keep them in the dairy herd. The slaughter provided freezer beef for the hired men as well. Now we were told that the four sides of beef had been condemned by the Food and Drug Administration for having 800 parts per million of PBB.

The slaughterhouse was desperate to get rid of the tainted meat, so they sent it back to us, covered with a foul purple dye that would discourage anyone from trying to eat it. The question that haunted us all, of course, was whether the October beef—almost all of which we had eaten—was similarly tainted. It was a thought that had occurred to us during the early stages of the problem, when the nature of the contamination was still unknown. Now Rick and I would worry about the health of the children and our own health, anxious at the first sign of sickness. Except for Lisa's pneumonia last fall and a round of ear infections, none of us had any apparent cause to worry. But Dr. Fries's warning remained with us: little was known about the effects of the chemical on human beings, but its effects on animals were all too evident to us. Fortunately, neither Rick nor I cared for the usual scorched taste of home-pasteurized milk, so we had never used the milk from the bulk tank for our own drinking and cooking. Later we learned that the October beef had contained 20 ppm of PBB.

In three weeks Rick had more test data on the amount of PBB in the cows, and the information confirmed Fries's warning: the contaminant at this degree of concentration was not disappearing at the rate of half each eight weeks. Our milk showed far more PBB than would be expected under that optimistic formula. Rick took the figures home with him to examine in detail over lunch, but the message was clear from the beginning: the only option left to us was to destroy the entire herd. While arrangements for that were going on, the cattle would have to be dried up, and the agony of producing eight thousand quarts of milk each day only to pump it out into the hardwood stand would finally come to an end. A livestock appraiser was called in to look over each cow on the lot while Rick shuffled through the pedigree sheets, reading back the information for each of the animals. All of them represented hours of planning, selective breeding, careful feeding, milking, health care and maintenance. Without a blink the appraiser judged each animal before him like a vintner judging wine, and wrote a number in his totebook. He gave us a copy of notes, collected his fees, and left Rick to assess the monetary loss: four hundred animals, none appraised at less than $900. From a farm that had supported seven families and produced enough milk for a city of 20,000 people, we had been reduced to virtually nothing.

Thirty of the most highly contaminated cows went to Michigan State University for a research experiment. As the cattle hauler loaded them up, one of the last of the Red Danish cows, a chestnut-coated pet named Scarface, was the final cow to walk up the ramp. The small animal stopped in the middle of her walk and turned around, looking almost questioningly at Rick and his father. It was as if she were searching for some sign of hope, some promise that the university's research, so lately undertaken, would find a cure for the contaminant.

Drying up the cows was not difficult but watching the process was hard for the men, and they spent as little time as they could around the cows. There was no way of explaining to the animals why their daily routine had changed. At milking times, they hung around the gates of their barns, lowing and looking for someone to relieve the pressure of the milk they had produced. For animals who had been producing fifty, sixty, even eighty pounds of milk a day, the absence of the twice-daily relief for their pendulous, swollen udders was painful. Once the drying-up had been completed, the barns were silent.

If we did recover from the loss of the cattle and begin a new herd, the barns would have to be given a thorough cleaning to remove as much of the residual PBB as humanly possible. To do that, it would be necessary to find some place to put the cows while waiting for the state or Farm Bureau Services to take them to a kill site. Rick and Ted and Mark decided that the best place would be the small marl pit pasture, which they had once used for a summer hospital grazing area for injured cattle. There was not enough grass there to keep the herd going, so the men decided to feed the dying and condemned cows extra hay. It was the least we could do after they had fed us for so many years.

Filling the pasture took days, for we could no longer afford to hire a cattle hauler, and each load only added eight cows to pitiful group milling about in the grassy space. Some of the cows were so weak when they were unloaded that they couldn't stay on their feet. A number of the animals resembled the starving cattle from the drought-stricken Sahel, their hides looking as if they were thrown over their bones. Dozens of them had lost patches of hair on their necks and faces; and the exposed skin resembled elephant hide. There were regular telephone calls from passersby reporting that one of the cows was stuck in the marl; always the same one would wade into the pool for a drink and get stuck in the soft bottom, her legs too weak to pull themselves loose. After several trips to the pasture to pull her out Rick began to wonder whether she had not intuited her ultimate fate and tried to speed the process along.

There were also the unkind remarks. As the weeks dragged by with no disposal site chosen, I began driving by different routes to reach Battle Creek so I could avoid the sight of the suffering animals. One nearby store owner remarked to me on the sad shape the cows were in and then added viperously, "My Daddy kept a few cows in his day, but he said that too many cows on a place just meant that they were getting poor care while the farmer was getting rich off their misery." Biting my tongue, I finished my shopping vowing never to return to that store, but convinced that nothing I would have said could have made a difference anyway. The media had picked up the story; news of the contamination was in the paper nearly every night; charges and countercharges were flying. All of the coverage had made experts out of the people with little or no experience with the problem, and telephoned suggestions came at all hours. For nine months of agony we had been left alone; I wished fervently we could be left alone now.

On impulse one day I drove the children to the barn where Flopsy was waiting for her third calf to be born. Every time I had asked Rick if Flopsy had gotten the feed, he hadn't answered me. I had taken these silences to mean that he was not sure, and I was encouraged to hear that the pet was still in the barn. Surely, Rick did not mean to send Flopsy to a mass grave somewhere. Parking the car by the milkhouse, we walked back to the nearly empty barn, the fine dust in the driveway sifting into our tennis shoes. The pile of wood scraps next to the barn door announced that the barn was still new; the children picked the scraps up as if they were treasure, and pocketed them thoughtfully. The double-wide barn lay before us, and I was awed by its size, though I had seen it before. The handful of cows inside the two-hundred-cow barn made it seem even bigger. **143**

We walked down the drive-through alley that had been planned for the feeder truck. On either side of us lay hundred-cow lots, the freestalls still pale-wood-new. "Let's see who can find Flopsy first," I suggested. The two older girls ran ahead, swooping down on the feeding cows.

"Don't run in the barn—you'll scare the cows!" The children slowed to a crawl, bending in curiosity to read the cow identification tags, and examining the long faces for the familiar white star.

"Here she is!" Kristen exclaimed, hugging a long-faced cow who stood about midway along the feeder. By the time I reached the patient cow, the children were piling feed in front of her and stroking her outstretched neck and long face. Soon there was a pile of silage in front of her, and all three children were patting her from every angle that they could reach. As I drew nearer to the pet cow, I saw with horror that there was hair missing on Flopsy's neck. I came closer, to pat the cow and to look; maybe she had just rubbed herself there, or maybe she had ringworm. I felt my throat tighten—there was little doubt now that the gentle cow had fallen prey to the poisoning, just as the others had; my silent prayers that just this one cow be spared had been in vain. I ran a hand over the trusting, soft-eyed animal, wondering desperately how she might be saved.

I looked more closely at the bare spots in Flopsy's hide; there was too much resemblance to the patches caused by the poisoning to dismiss them, but there was no sign of the "elephant hide" we had seen in many of the animals that were now in the marl pit pasture. Maybe Rick was holding Flopsy back at the barn until he was sure that the bare patches were a sign of the poisoning—or maybe he had already figured out a way to save her from the mass grave that the state had proposed for the contaminated cows. The gentle cow was oblivious to my frantic thoughts, and bunted me, looking for some scratching or a treat. "I don't have any treats with me, old girl, but I'll give your ears a good scratching," I said, trying to brush back the tears that had begun to form at the corners of my eyes. If I began to cry, Stephanie was sure to catch on, and once she understood Kristen and Lisa would soon discover that their pet

was poisoned. After a very long time, I called to the children and told them to say good-bye to the gentle cow which had happily endured their childish display of affection. As we walked back out of the big barn to the car, I looked back to the spot where we had left Flopsy. The small, droopy-eared cow still stood watching us; all of the other cows around her had gone back to feeding.

"We went to the barn today to see Flopsy!" The children were telling Rick as he came down the hill toward the silo with the feeder truck. He waved them aside and parked the truck on the concrete floor of the silo so that it could be loaded for the next feeding, and walked back with us toward the milkhouse.

When the children had run on far ahead, I turned to Rick and asked, "Did Flopsy get the feed, too? She had patches on her neck where there is no hair." My voice was choked off by a lump in my throat.

"I was hoping you wouldn't notice," he said quietly. "She has the poisoning, too. I wasn't sure until just recently, but those patches are getting bigger, just like they did in the others. I don't know what to do. The state is going to require us to have every contaminated animal removed from the farm and destroyed. They already have milk samples from us, with the numbers of the cows represented in the sample in their records. I've thought of everything, and I keep coming back to the same answer."

"Will she have to go to the kill site, too?" I asked, and looked down, knowing I could not avoid the answer.

"Either that, or go to the university with the thirty cows we're saving for research. I'm just as sorry as you are—but I can't see how we could keep her on the place. If the state knew that we kept one contaminated cow, they'd never lift our quarantine!" He stopped and looked down at the dust around his feet. "I want to get this whole thing behind us as fast as I can, and go on with a new herd. Even the animals with a personality are going to have to go."

Rick fell silent, and we walked the rest of the way to the milkhouse without saying anything, each of us pondering the unknown and frightening future.

When we reached the car, I broke the silence. "I want you to explain this to the children—I don't think that I can."

"When the time comes, I will; I think that they might have some inkling of what's going on right now. We haven't kept those phone calls a secret. They already know that we can't sell milk—they asked me why we had that milk truck by the barn all the time now, and I told them."

"Do you think that they understand?"

"I don't even know if I understand it myself."

With the cattle gone from the barn, the men took turns going out to the pasture to feed them and began the methodical process of trying to clean the buildings. From each individual freestall the sawdust bedding had to be removed and the dirt foundation scraped out. A team of men went through with a pressure washer, cleaning the railings, the posts, and the feeders. The plan was to resurface the cement floors of the feeders when possible to try to restrict the movement of the toxin from interstices in the concrete. Rick knew that they would never be able to get all of the chemical out of the barn; the posts the cows had rubbed against when they scratched themselves were probably carrying PBB from their body oils. But we had to do something; we could not simply sit back and wait for the mess to be sorted out by the insurance companies, bureaucrats, and hucksters of false hope.

When the barns were cleaned, Rick and his father would go to the bank to try to negotiate a loan to meet the payroll and payments. If we could manage it, we hoped to restock one of the cleaned barns with new heifers from Wisconsin. When the new animals started producing, perhaps the Department of Agriculture would allow us to ship milk again. It was a small hope, but enough to keep us going.

The night before the cattle haulers were scheduled to take the cattle away the children prayed that the trucks would get lost on the way. Heavy-hearted I listened to them plot to save their favorite.

"We could take Flopsy and hide in the woods," Kristen suggested.

"We'd have to sneak her some food. And how could we get her away from Grandpa's pasture without anyone knowing?" Stephanie, almost six, had a tendency to ask the difficult, practical questions.

"Maybe we could get Mama to take us to Grandma's house and then we could sneak away to get Flopsy," Kristen persisted.

"But how would we get Flopsy across the road?" Stephanie wondered.

"You could take her out of the pasture across the road, and we could wait for you on the other side. Then we could take Flopsy to the woods."

I couldn't listen any longer. I had no idea how much of the tragedy the children really grasped. I knew that Rick had told Stephanie that all the cows would have to be killed, but, despite the incident a few weeks earlier with the dead calf, I didn't know how that registered with her. Tears in my eyes, I went downstairs to Rick. "I want you to hear this: the children are plotting to save Flopsy."

He followed me up the stairs to hear the rest of the scheme being discussed in the darkness.

"Maybe Uncle Mark would help us," Stephanie was saying. "He could bring Flopsy to our house in the red truck. She couldn't walk all the way here anyway."

"And we could ride in the red truck, too," Lisa added, excitedly.

Stephanie bounced out of bed and began to tiptoe out of the room. As she rounded the corner by her door, Rick caught her. Trying to sound stern he said, "Where are you going? You're supposed to be in bed sleeping."

"I was going to call Uncle Mark," she whispered and began

to cry. Rick took the sobbing child in his arms and carried her back into her room.

"I know you're unhappy about Flopsy having to go away with the other cows tomorrow; I'm unhappy about it too. We have to let the cows all go, because they're very sick—so sick that we can't make them better again. We can't use their milk, and we can't let them have calves. If we can't sell their milk, we just don't have any money left to feed them. Flopsy and the other cows are going to a place where other sick cows from other farms will be, so that the doctors can look at all of them together."

"Will they make them better?" Kristen asked.

"I don't know, Kristen. I don't know." He spent a long time in the dark room, holding the three children in turn and talking to them. I had gone downstairs to cry alone, not wanting to upset the children now that Rick had calmed them. When he finally came down, I was sitting in the darkened living room.

"Don't turn the light on unless you want to read," I said. "I'd just as soon sit in the dark."

"No, no reading tonight," he said. "I guess this is it."

Late the next afternoon, after the trucks had left and the cows were gone, Rick and Mark had gone to the strangely silent milkhouse and sat in the barn office trying to comprehend what had happened. From the shelves and window-sills, production and management trophies mocked their despair. They began to recall the details of the nightmare.

"I remember the first calf we took to the diagnostic lab at MSU," Rick said softly. "They just put an alligator clip on the lip of the calf and another one on his tail, as though they were testing a piece of equipment. Then they plugged him into a wall outlet with an ordinary extension cord. That current alone was enough to drop him." Rick's voice was soft, and dropped away to a whisper before he paused.

"Remember how we went up to see the cows in the experiment just after the first cutting of hay?" he continued, looking out the window at the traffic hurrying by on M37. "It was almost festive. I thought they might be able to find something that would help the cows pass the chemical out of their systems. I felt hopeful about the future. We went into the barn where the cows were, and I was nearly torn apart at seeing them again."

Rick's voice was sad and softer now as he recalled the two neat rows of cows in the university dairy barn, their heads held fast in stanchions.

"The cows were strange, subdued—they didn't seem to remember us. The Holsteins were gray and black instead of white and black. I walked down the rows looking at the individual cows; some of them were missing already. Finally, I found someone who had worked with the cows and asked him why they were so quiet. He told me that they were trying phenobarbital on them to force their livers to excrete the toxin more quickly. The gray color came from the powdered charcoal they added to their feed to absorb the excreted toxin. The phenobarbital made them subdued. The cows that were missing had been sacrificed already. One of them had fought the stanchion and hurt her legs. They had fed her to minks to see how they would react to the poison.

"I asked the man in the barn what they were going to do with the rest of the cows, and he said they'd sacrifice them and incinerate them at the Vet Clinic. We sent them up there with hope—and there was no hope, no reprieve. I had to get out of the barn; it was like death row. The experiment had failed, and the rest was inevitable."

When Rick had fallen silent, Mark turned to him. "I went to see Scarface a week ago—she's the only one left now; the others have died or been sacrificed. She was off the drug and remembered me. I felt like a criminal, sending her there to die among strangers."

Epilogue

SHORTLY AFTER George Fries notified the US Department of Agriculture in Washington about the chemical contaminant in the FBS #402 we had shipped him for testing, the Michigan Department of Agriculture was contacted. The next day, MDA personnel began collecting milk samples from tank truck loads arriving at dairies around the state and, with the help of the Food and Drug Administration, also began to check feed mills for contamination by PBB. On April 30, 1974, an unopened bag of Firemaster was found in the Farm Bureau Mendon Cooperative. The bag had been shipped from the Farm Bureau's Battle Creek, Michigan mill. This provided the only concrete proof that the shipping mixup had actually occurred. When PBB showed up in both the milk and feed samples, agriculture department officials notified Michigan Governor William Milliken, and the State Department of Public Health.

On May 10, 1974, fifteen dairy herds, including ours, were quarantined, removing their products from the marketplace. At this time, the Food and Drug Administration set an administrative guideline of 1.0 parts per million as the maximum amount of PBB allowed in milk. (1.0 ppm would be comparable to one yard in the total 590-mile distance between Detroit and Des Moines, Iowa.) By May 13, fourteen other dairy herds, two beef herds, three poultry flocks, and one swine herd had also been quarantined. When the tolerance was set, the FDA said that it could only test reliably for the chemical above that amount. An important consideration was the presence in the compound of bromine, a chemical known to cause liver damage. It was first thought that the 1.0 ppm tolerance would be sufficient to protect the public from significant amounts of PBB.

In an attempt to assess the scope of the PBB problem, MDA called a scientific meeting to bring together representatives from USDA, FDA, Michigan State University, Michigan Chemical Company, Farm Bureau Services, Michigan Department of Public Health and the Michigan Attorney General. Drawing on information gathered at this meeting, the Michigan Commission on Agriculture proposed emergency legislation which would pay the quarantined farmer for his loss of animals and income due to the PBB contamination. Under the proposed legislation, MDA would be permitted to condemn the contaminated animals and authorize indemnity payments to their owners. Then MDA would enter into civil suits against the parties responsible for the contamination.

However, on June 6, 1974, Michigan Attorney General Frank Kelley told MDA that it had no authority to order livestock condemned unless the condemnation was required to halt the spread of infection or contagious disease. The MDA was also advised that it had no authority to pay an indemnity to farmers whose animals had been contaminated by toxic chemicals. After looking into the possibility of federal help with the contamination, the MDA reported to the Governor's office that there was little hope of federal assistance with the problem.

On June 7, 1974, the FDA established guidelines in meat and meat products of 1.0 ppm of PBB. By the middle of June 1974, seven hundred tons of contaminated feed had been seized by the MDA. Ultimately, this feed was destroyed.

July 2, 1974, sixty-five days after the PBB contamination was discovered on April 26, 1974, and fifty-three days after the first dairy herds were quarantined, Michigan Public Act 181 was enacted, establishing a burial site for contaminated livestock. In the next two days 116 head of cattle were destroyed and buried at Kalkaska.

The Kalkaska site was chosen because it was located in a relatively inaccessible portion of state land and in an area where the deep water table and soil composition would presumably prevent the spread of the fire retardant into human water supplies or private property. There was, however, opposition from the residents of the township in which the site was located—no one wanted such a disposal area near him. Several residents feared for the safety of their water supply.

Once the contaminated livestock was picked up from an unused feedlot near Mount Pleasant and another holding area near Fremont, the animals were hauled in small groups to a holding area in a clearing in the dense second growth pine forest in north-central Michigan. Unloaded into a strangely nonfarm atmosphere after a jolting ride of hundreds of miles, the cattle, hogs, sheep and chickens could not comprehend the fate that lay in store for them.

A short distance from the holding area, heavy machinery scooped out long 15 foot deep trenches in the clearing. One by one, the animals were removed from the holding pens, injected with succinylcholine chloride, a powerful muscle relaxant which immobilized them and suffocated them by paralyzing the muscles of their diaphragms. The euthanized animal was then shot with a rifle and lifted into the air by the jaws of a log-handling machine, which dropped the body into one of the deep trenches, where its abdominal cavity and rumen (or stomach) would be slashed open to permit gases to escape. The carcasses were put in a single layer in the trenches, and were covered to within three feet of the ground level with sand. A foot deep layer of bentonite was put over the sand to seal the burial pit and topsoil put over the bentonite.

After a year and a half of operation, the burial site at Kalkaska contained 23,671 cattle, 4,621 swine, 1,399 sheep, 656 chickens, 2 goats, 32 rabbits, and 6 horses. In addition, 865 tons of feed were destroyed and reported to the MDA, along with 17,944 pounds of cheese, 2,634 pounds of butter, 34,000 pounds of dry milk and 403,936 dozen eggs.

(A second burial site is being prepared in the summer of 1978 near Mio, Michigan. This burial site, projected for an additional 5,000 animals, consists of a 50 foot deep pit lined by 20 feet of clay on the top and all sides. Animals taken to the Mio site will probably be those which are condemned under Public Act 77.)

As soon as the cleaning of the empty dairy barn at the Halbert farm was finished, Ted and Rick Halbert approached their bank about a loan. After paying outstanding bills and meeting their payroll obligations, they began to purchase bred heifers (animals which have never calved but will calve in the next few months) from Wisconsin. It would be several years before they regained the milk production they had before September 1973. Their selective breeding program was buried at Kalkaska.

While the wheels of state government slowly began to turn toward coping with the disaster, quarantined farms were forced to struggle with the daily feed and care of animals which were no longer a source of income. Like the Halberts, dozens of Michigan farmers found themselves in the desperate situation of trying to survive the daily loss of years of hard work, and a continual drain of thousands of dollars of capital. It was painfully evident that they would not be able to endure this insane reality for very long—but help was not forthcoming.

By the fall of 1974, the first insurance settlements involving PBB contamination were paid by carriers for Farm Bureau Services and Michigan Chemical Company. Among the claims settled for the loss of livestock and lost milk production was one for the Halbert farm. Of nine hundred claims filed against Michigan Chemical Company and Farm Bureau Services, six hundred claims were settled by February 1977 for a total of $38,000,000.

Meanwhile, the laboratory testing procedures used by MDA and FDA were constantly being refined. On November 4, 1974, the FDA lowered the tolerance for PBB in meat and milk from 1.0 ppm to 0.3 ppm (about the equivalent of one yard out of the entire 1700-mile distance from Los Angeles to Des Moines, Iowa).

With the lowering of the PBB tolerance, an additional 346 farms were drawn into the disaster. This tenfold increase in quarantined farms expanded the scope of the disaster to parts of Michigan which had been thought to be free of the contaminant. As the situation worsened, MDA Director Ball sent a letter to the Secretary of Agriculture in Washington requesting that the PBB problem be declared a national emergency. Ball also requested emergency funds to help Michigan deal with the growing problem. The requests were denied.

Trapped with their now-useless livestock and unable to get immediate financial assistance or insurance settlements, recently quarantined farmers found a powerful ally in the press. During the winter of 1975, farmers illustrated their plight by taking their sick and dying animals to the lawn of the state capitol in Lansing. When the display of animals in shocking ill health did not bring a satisfactory result, several farmers banded together to destroy their own cattle before horrified reporters and television cameramen. The tragic scene was to be repeated for the next year and a half. One unfortunate farmer from Coopersville, Gerald Woltjer, found that his recently purchased farm had been one of the original highly contaminated premises. Faced with mysterious ailments in his dairy herd and mounting expenses, Woltjer shot two hundred of his cattle in one night. Other farmers who faced similar economic straits found that they were unable to bear the agony of destroying **153** livestock they had raised almost as a second family. In several cases quarantined neighbors traded the macabre task of killing each other's livestock.

Alarmed by the farmer protests that the tolerance level for PBB in animal products was still too high, consumer groups began to ask their grocery stores for meat that could be proven to be free of the fire retardant—or for meat that was produced out of state. In response, several store chains began to advertise that they sold only "western beef." A large supermarket chain based in Grand Rapids, Michigan, considered using the "western beef" advertisement both in the print and broadcast media. Other stores simply added signs of varying sizes and subtleties in their meat departments. Frequently, the small "western beef" sign by the supermarket meat case could be interpreted by the consumer as "PBB free," "not grown in Michigan" or of a certain quality the buyer associated with the western beef producers.

Consumer alarm over the safety of Michigan's food supply and the continued farmer protests that the PBB tolerance in foods was still too high urged Michigan Governor William Milliken to press MDA Director Ball for public hearings on the subject. Hearings were held in Lansing on May 29, 1975 and June 10, 1976 to attempt to assess the safety of the state's animal products, but scientific data on the industrial chemical and its effects on humans and animals was sadly lacking. As a result of the hearings, the Michigan Commission of Agriculture concluded that the weight of available scientific evidence did not support a lowering of the tolerance for PBB in animal products.

While the pressure on the tolerance continued, attempts were underway to begin a study of the human health questions which had been raised by the widespread contamination. In November 1976, more than three years after the initial PBB contamination occurred, a study was initiated on farm families who had consumed contaminated animal products. Shortly after the disaster was uncovered in April 1974, a University of Michigan researcher named Dr. Thomas Corbett ran his own series of experiments on mice, and was alarmed to find that the chemical apparently caused increased liver weights and birth defects in some of their offspring. Corbett presented his findings

to an October 1974 meeting of state officials in East Lansing, and also to noted environmental medicine specialist Dr. Irving Selikoff, of New York City's Mount Sinai Medical Center. Dr. Corbett asked Dr. Selikoff if he would be willing to bring a medical team to Michigan to study the effects of the PBB contamination. Selikoff, an internationally known expert on human health effects of industrial contaminants, said that he would bring a medical team to the state if he was formally invited by the state.

But for a year and a half, the Selikoff offer was not acted upon. In the meantime, Michigan health officials surveyed PBB contaminated farmers and concluded that there were no ill effects that could be conclusively linked to PBB exposure. Finally, Edie Clark, an aide to Representative Bobby Crim, rediscovered the dormant Selikoff offer and urged Speaker Crim to act upon it. The result was a formal invitation from the Michigan Legislature and Governor Milliken to Selikoff to initiate a study of the affected farm families.

The resulting study includes 1,029 farmers, their families and others who had eaten contaminated animal products.

Played against a backdrop of frustration, politics, scientific questioning and speculation, the Grand Rapids study spotlighted the Selikoff research team, a group of young medical specialists finally dropped into the festering PBB situation like the cavalry in an old western movie. Led by the unflappable silver-haired Selikoff, the team of doctors worked long hours to conduct an exhaustive battery of tests on the people who lined the corridors of one emptied floor of Kent Community Hospital. Strapped by limited funds and flooded by requests for examinations by walk-ins and referrals, the medical team was forced to add more than a score of volunteers to its staff to handle routine paperwork, route people to examining areas, hold children for blood tests, conduct a nursery for children whose parents were being examined and many other jobs during the week. Taken from the population of people who were most affected by the contamination, the volunteers reflected the diverse opinions of the farm community. Slipping among the lines in the hallways were several journalists and television reporters, hoping for a story. Somehow, in the seeming chaos and the stacks of samples being labelled and cooled, the process of information gathering managed to retain a respect for the individual.

In January 1977, the Selikoff team issued a preliminary report of its findings. In its preliminary report, the Selikoff team found that 37 percent of the people examined experienced neurological abnormalities including memory loss, extreme fatigue, lack of coordination, and numbness. Some of the people examined also showed abnormalities of the liver in the examination. Various symptoms that Selikoff was reluctant to link to PBB including skin rashes, mental stress, liver abnormalities, and indications of damage to white blood cells, which might cause a weakening to the body's resistance to disease, are still under study by the New York-based medical team.

With the research started on the PBB-exposed farm population, the Selikoff team returned to Michigan in May of 1978 to test a sampling of Michigan's general population. Selikoff cautioned that findings from the farm study should not be applied to the general population study, for the farmers were highly exposed to the chemical, while the general population was exposed to a much lesser degree.

As research continues, no agent has been found to remove the chemical from the human body; nursing mothers who fear that they might pass PBB to their infants through their milk can obtain breast milk sampling kits through their doctors or local public health clinics. Ominous signs that PBB will be a long-term health threat have begun to appear. Dr. B. N. Gupta, working at the National Institute of Environmental Health Sciences, has found that seven laboratory rats out of several hundred involved in PBB toxicology tests developed malignant tumors. The affected animals were less than one year old and had malignancies involving the urinary bladder, liver and lymph systems. Dr. Gupta says that "PBB is definitely carcinogenic." Meanwhile, the highly exposed farm population is being observed for any incidence of common symptoms, and silently clinging to the hope that someone, somewhere, will find a way to rid them of the burden they carry invisibly in their tissues. In many families, a grim joke prevails at the sign of physical or emotional symptoms: "It must be your PBB acting up again."

Nearly four years after the accidental mixing of the industrial fire retardant in cattle feed, a damage suit against Michigan Chemical Company and Farm Bureau Services finally came to trial. The suit, filed by dairyman Roy Tacoma of Falmouth, Michigan, was to carry the accumulated frustrations and hopes of many aggrieved farmers who had been forced to wait through years of legal hassling for an end to the economic troubles wrought by the contamination. Throughout the fourteen-month-long trial, a small knot of similarly distressed farmers gathered daily to watch the proceedings. Whatever the outcome of the Tacoma trial, the precedent of its decision would affect their futures as well as the Tacomas'. The Tacoma trial, generating tens of thousands of pages of written testimony, became the longest-running trial in Michigan judicial history.

In an attempt to deal with consumer hysteria and continued pressure by farmers who claimed that they and their animals had suffered with low level contamination to PBB, Representative Spaniola introduced House Bill 4109 on February 10, 1977. The intent of HB4109 was to lower the tolerance level of PBB to .02 parts per million (roughly comparable to one yard of 1½ times the distance around the circumference of the earth) and to indemnify farmers for livestock which must be destroyed under the lower tolerance.

On August 4, 1977, HB4109 emerged from Michigan's legislative process as Public Act 77. When the new law became effective on October 3, 1977, its immediate result was to place under scrutiny every dairy cow in the state that had been born before January 1, 1976, at the time of her removal from a dairy herd for slaughter. Should a fat biopsy done on such a cow exceed the new lowered standard for meat, the owner of the animal would be reimbursed for the full market value of the animal. The animal itself would be taken to the state disposal site and humanely destroyed and buried.

Also under Public Act 77 the milk produced on every one of the state's 9,000 dairy farms was to be tested by February 1978. On February 3, 1978, the Michigan Department of Agriculture announced that only one of the farms in the state was in violation. By early April 1978, the MDA tissue sampling program had processed nearly 45,000 tissue samples, finding 781 in violation of the new guideline. In mid-April 1978, Michigan's entire upper peninsula was exempted from the PBB testing program by a concurrent resolution of the Michigan legislature.

As the 1978 spring planting season begins, farmers on thirty Michigan farms face the new season with more than the usual burden of hopes and problems. The men who farm the thirty most highly contaminated farms have begun the new season with some apprehension of the future for their businesses, and, because in much of today's farming the family is still involved, their own and their families' futures as well. Early in 1978, an MDA experiment on the Halbert farm showed that the young stock—the offspring of cattle which were purchased to replace the original contaminated herd—were showing more PBB than officials in the MDA had expected. When other farms in the thirty most highly contaminated farms were similarly tested, MDA men found that many of them showed a residual amount of the fire retardant. Apparently, the new animals were picking the PBB up from the environment in which the original condemned animals had lived. Current attempts to pinpoint the sources of the residual contamination have so far proven inconclusive.

What residual contamination could mean to the affected farms, at the worst, is a rerun of the cycle of having their animals quarantined, their products declared unsalable, and worst of all, having their barns, fields and pastures declared unfit for animal husbandry or crop production. To many, the loss would be unthinkable—especially when added to the burden of the original loss of their animals and the emotional and physiological uncertainty of carrying the exotic chemical in their own bodies as well. Rather than buckling under the load, the farmers have gone on with their spring work, trying to avoid the unthinkable. Some have not planted crops in fields they think might be contaminated by the spreading of PBB-laced manure from their original, now-destroyed herds. A study of PBB uptake done by George Fries, the animal scientist from the Beltsville, Maryland USDA facility, indicates that sheep grazing on pastures which had been contaminated by the chemical may pick up the chemical from the contaminated soil. Fries contaminated two pasures with PBB in the fall of 1975, and put 10 sheep on each of them in April of 1976, allowing the sheep to graze in the pastures until October 1976. During the grazing time, Fries replaced half of the sheep in each pasture and kept the other half on the contaminated lots the full six months. From the soil, which was experimentally contaminated with PBB, the sheep acquired up to 800 parts per billion PBB, depending on the amount of time they stayed in the contaminated pastures—40 times more than allowed by law. Another ominous twist is the discovery that PBB is collecting in the furnace filters of houses on affected farms and that deer and rabbits on contaminated farms are showing up to 500% more than the legal amount of PBB in food.

158

Clearly, these findings do not bode well for farms which have a residual amount of the chemical in their buildings, fields or pastures. As of spring, 1978, seven of the highest level contaminated farms are being monitored for possible residual contamination by the Michigan Department of Agriculture. Only the passage of time and more testing will determine the fates of these farms and the people whose livelihood they provide.

Where, then, does the PBB story find us in mid-1978? The Michigan Department of Agriculture says that the state's food supply is now free of any significant amount of the chemical. The problem no one wants to mention is the massive exposure that occurred before the accident was recognized—that nearly everyone living the the state in 1973–1974 was exposed, to some degree, to the exotic chemical, and that is the worrisome question which the Selikoff study and the long-range Michigan

Department of Public Health address. It will be years before all the questions are answered. Until then, all we can do is wait and hope that we have contained this disaster, that someone will come up with a way to rid the human body of this chemical, that we are not the victims of our own technology.